It's another great book from CGP...

GCSE Core Science is all about **understanding how science works**. And not only that — understanding it well enough to be able to **question** what you hear on TV and read in the papers.

But don't panic. This book includes all the **science facts** you need to learn, and shows you how they work in the real world. It even includes a **free** Online Edition you can read on your computer or tablet.

How to get your free Online Edition

Just go to **cgpbooks.co.uk/extras** and enter this code...

4400 9126 4379 8098

By the way, this code only works for one person. If somebody else has used this book before you, they might have already claimed the Online Edition.

CGP — still the best! ☺

Our sole aim here at CGP is to produce the highest quality books — carefully written, immaculately presented and dangerously close to being funny.

Then we work our socks off to get them out to you — at the cheapest possible prices.

Contents

Published by CGP

From original material by Richard Parsons.

Editors:
Charlotte Burrows, Katherine Craig, Ben Fletcher, Helena Hayes, Felicity Inkpen,
Rosie McCurrie, Edmund Robinson, Jane Sawers, Karen Wells, Sarah Williams.

Contributors:
Mike Bossart, James Foster, Jim Wilson.

ISBN: 978 1 84146 719 1

With thanks to Sarah Blackwood, Helen Brace, Katie Braid, Janet Cruse-Sawyer, Chris Elliss,
Ian Francis, Glenn Rogers and Hayley Thompson for the proofreading.
With thanks to Jan Greenway, Laura Jakubowski and Laura Stoney for the copyright research.

Image on page 83 courtesy of NASA Ames Research Center.

With thanks to Science Photo Library for permission to use the image on page 84.

Pages 50, 70, 81 and 99 contain public sector information published by the Health and Safety
Executive and licensed under the Open Government Licence v1.0.

Every effort has been made to locate copyright holders and obtain permission to reproduce
sources. For those sources where it has been difficult to trace the originator of the work,
we would be grateful for information. If any copyright holder would like us to make an
amendment to the acknowledgements, please notify us and we will gladly update the book
at the next reprint. Thank you.

Printed by Elanders Ltd, Newcastle upon Tyne.
Clipart from Corel®

The Scientific Process

You need to know a few things about how the world of science works. First up is the <u>scientific process</u> — how a scientist's <u>mad idea</u> turns into a <u>widely accepted theory</u>.

Scientists Come Up with Hypotheses — Then Test Them

About 100 years ago, scientists hypothesised that atoms looked like this.

1) Scientists try to <u>explain</u> things. Everything.

2) They start by <u>observing</u> something they don't understand — it could be anything, e.g. planets in the sky, a person suffering from an illness, what matter is made of... anything.

3) Then, they come up with a <u>hypothesis</u> — a <u>possible explanation</u> for what they've observed.

4) The next step is to <u>test</u> whether the hypothesis might be <u>right or not</u> — this involves <u>gathering evidence</u> (i.e. <u>data</u> from <u>investigations</u>).

5) To gather evidence the scientist uses the hypothesis to make a <u>prediction</u> — a statement based on the hypothesis that can be <u>tested</u>.

6) If data from experiments or studies <u>backs up the prediction</u>, you're one step closer to figuring out if the hypothesis is true.

Other Scientists Will Test the Hypotheses Too

1) <u>Other</u> scientists will use the hypothesis to make their <u>own predictions</u>, and carry out their <u>own experiments</u> or studies.

2) They'll also try to <u>reproduce</u> the original investigations to check the results.

3) And if <u>all the experiments</u> in the world back up the hypothesis, then scientists start to think it's <u>true</u>.

4) However, if a scientist somewhere in the world does an experiment that <u>doesn't</u> fit with the hypothesis (and other scientists can <u>reproduce</u> these results), then the hypothesis is in trouble.

5) When this happens, scientists have to come up with a new hypothesis (maybe a <u>modification</u> of the old hypothesis, or maybe a completely <u>new</u> one).

After more evidence was gathered scientists changed their hypothesis to this.

If Evidence Supports a Hypothesis, It's Accepted — for Now

1) If pretty much every scientist in the world believes a hypothesis to be true because experiments back it up, then it usually goes in the <u>textbooks</u> for students to learn.

2) Accepted hypotheses are often referred to as <u>theories</u>.

Now we think it's more like this.

3) Our <u>currently accepted</u> theories are the ones that have survived this 'trial by evidence' — they've been tested many, many times over the years and survived (while the less good ones have been ditched).

4) However... they never, <u>never</u> become hard and fast, totally indisputable <u>fact</u>. You can never know... it'd only take <u>one</u> odd, totally inexplicable result, and the hypothesising and testing would start all over again.

You expect me to believe that — then show me the evidence...

Scientific <u>ideas</u> are <u>changing</u> all the time as a result of <u>new evidence</u> being uncovered. It's the role of the <u>scientific community</u> (all the world's scientists) to <u>test</u> and <u>evaluate</u> these ideas and decide whether or not they should be <u>accepted</u> as theories — so you don't have to waste your time learning stuff that's absolute rubbish.

Your Data's Got to Be Good

Evidence is the key to science — but not all evidence is equally good.
The way evidence is <u>gathered</u> can have a big effect on how <u>trustworthy</u> it is...

Lab Experiments and Studies Are Better Than Rumour

1) Results from <u>controlled experiments</u> in <u>laboratories</u> are <u>great</u>. A lab is the easiest place to <u>control</u> variables so that they're all kept <u>constant</u> (except for the one you're investigating). This makes it easier to carry out a <u>fair test</u>.

There's more about variables and fair tests on page 5.

2) For things that you <u>can't investigate in the lab</u> (e.g. climate) you conduct <u>scientific studies</u>. As many of the variables as possible are controlled, to make it a fair test.

3) Old wives' tales, rumours, hearsay, "what someone said", and so on, should be taken with a pinch of salt. Without any evidence they're <u>NOT scientific</u> — they're just <u>opinions</u>.

The Bigger the Sample Size the Better

Data based on <u>small samples</u> isn't as good as data based on large samples.
A sample should be <u>representative</u> of the <u>whole population</u> (i.e. it should share as many of the various characteristics in the population as possible) — a small sample can't do that as well.

Evidence Needs to be Reliable (Reproducible)

Evidence is only reliable if <u>other people can repeat it</u>. If they can't, then you can't believe it.

RELIABLE means that the data can be <u>reproduced by others</u>.

<u>EXAMPLE:</u> In 1989, two scientists claimed that they'd produced '<u>cold fusion</u>' (the energy source of the <u>Sun</u> — but <u>without</u> the <u>enormous temperatures</u>). It was huge news — if true, this could have meant energy from <u>seawater</u> — the ideal energy solution for the world... forever. However, other scientists just <u>couldn't</u> get the <u>same results</u> — i.e. the results weren't <u>reliable</u>. And until they are, 'cold fusion' isn't going to be generally accepted as <u>fact</u>.

Evidence Also Needs to Be Valid

VALID means that the data is <u>reliable</u> AND <u>answers the original question</u>.

<u>EXAMPLE: DO POWER LINES CAUSE CANCER?</u>
Some studies have found that children who live near <u>overhead power lines</u> are more likely to develop <u>cancer</u>. What they'd actually found was a <u>correlation</u> (relationship) between the variables "<u>presence of power lines</u>" and "<u>incidence of cancer</u>" — they found that as one changed, so did the other. But this evidence is <u>not enough</u> to say that the power lines <u>cause</u> cancer, as other explanations might be possible. For example, power lines are often near <u>busy roads</u>, so the areas tested could contain <u>different levels</u> of <u>pollution</u> from traffic. Also, you need to look at types of neighbourhoods and <u>lifestyles</u> of people living in the tested areas (could diet be a factor... or something else you hadn't thought of...). So these studies don't show a definite link and so don't <u>answer the original question</u>.

Does the data really say that?...

If it's so hard to be <u>definite</u> about anything, how does anybody <u>ever</u> get convinced about anything?
Well, what usually happens is that you get a <u>load</u> of evidence that all points the same way. If one study can't rule out a particular possibility, then maybe another one can. So you gradually build up a whole <u>body of evidence</u>, and it's this (rather than any single study) that convinces people.

Benefits, Risks and Decision Making

Science is all about the balance between benefit and risk — a bit like life really...

Developments in Science Usually Have Benefits and Drawbacks...

Scientists have created loads of new technologies that could improve our lives.
For example, generating electricity using nuclear power has lots of benefits:

1) The national population benefits from a reliable source of electricity.
2) There's a global benefit because generating electricity this way doesn't contribute to global warming (like coal-fired power stations do).
3) Construction companies benefit from years of work in building the power station.
4) Local people benefit from new jobs.

However, it's not all good news. One of the drawbacks is:

Nuclear power stations are very expensive. Perhaps the money that goes into building them would be better spent on things like building new wind turbines or hydroelectric plants.

...and They're Never Risk Free

1) Most technologies have some risks.
   For example, for a new nuclear power station:

   • Local people might suffer from higher radiation exposure, which could affect their health.

   • There could be a major accident, like the Chernobyl disaster, which would affect large areas.

2) To make a decision about a course of action (e.g. whether or not to build a new nuclear power station) society has to weigh up the benefits, drawbacks and risks involved for everyone.

Loads of Other Factors Can Influence Decisions Too

Here are some other factors that can influence decisions about science, and the way science is used:

Economic issues: Society can't always afford to do things scientists recommend without cutting back elsewhere (e.g. investing heavily in alternative energy sources).

Social issues: Decisions based on scientific evidence affect people — e.g. should fossil fuels be taxed more highly (to invest in alternative energy)? Should alcohol be banned (to prevent health problems)? Would the effect on people's lifestyles be acceptable...

Environmental issues: Genetically modified crops may help us produce more food — but some people think they could cause environmental problems.

Ethical issues: There are a lot of things that scientific developments have made possible, but should we do them? E.g. clone humans, develop better nuclear weapons.

Not revising — a definite drawback in the exam...

Developments in science involve a lot of weighing up — new technologies have risks, but the benefits are often huge. Then there are the economic, social, environmental and ethical issues to think about...

Science Has Limits

Science can give us amazing things — cures for diseases, space travel, heated toilet seats...
But science has its limitations — there are questions that it just can't answer.

Some Questions Are Unanswered by Science — So Far

1) We don't understand everything. And we never will. We'll find out more, for sure — as more hypotheses are suggested, and more experiments are done. But there'll always be stuff we don't know.

> **EXAMPLES:**
> * Today we don't know as much as we'd like about the impacts of global warming.
>   How much will sea level rise? And to what extent will weather patterns change?
> * We also don't know anywhere near as much as we'd like about the universe.
>   Are there other life forms out there? And what is the universe made of?

2) These are complicated questions. At the moment, scientists don't all agree on the answers because there isn't enough evidence.

3) But eventually, we probably will be able to answer these questions once and for all...
   ...all we need is more evidence.

4) But by then there'll be loads of new questions to answer.

Other Questions Are Unanswerable by Science

1) Then there's the other type... questions that all the experiments in the world won't help us answer — the "Should we be doing this at all?" type questions. There are always two sides...

2) Take embryo screening (which allows you to choose an embryo with particular characteristics). It's possible to do it — but does that mean we should?

3) Different people have different opinions.

> For example...
> * Some people say it's good... couples whose existing child needs a bone marrow transplant, but who can't find a donor, will be able to have another child selected for its matching bone marrow. This would save the life of their first child — and if they want another child anyway... where's the harm?
> * Other people say it's bad... they say it could have serious effects on the new child. In the above example, the new child might feel unwanted — thinking they were only brought into the world to help someone else. And would they have the right to refuse to donate their bone marrow (as anyone else would)?

> THE GAZETTE
> BONE MARROW BABY'S BROTHER SAVED
>
> THE POST
> BONE MARROW BABY BORN: WHAT RIGHTS DOES HE HAVE?

4) This question of whether something is morally or ethically right or wrong can't be answered by more experiments — there is no "right" or "wrong" answer.

5) The best we can do is get a consensus from society — a judgement that most people are more or less happy to live by. Science can provide more information to help people make this judgement, and the judgement might change over time. But in the end it's up to people and their conscience.

Chips or rice? — totally unanswerable by science...

Right — get this straight in your head — science can't tell you whether you should or shouldn't do something. That kind of thing is up to you and society to decide. There are tons of questions that science might be able to answer in the future — like how much sea level might rise due to global warming, what the Universe is made of and whatever happened to those pink stripy socks with Santa on that I used to have.

Planning Experiments

That's all the dull stuff about the world of science over — now to the hands-on part. The next few pages show how <u>experiments</u> should be carried out — by both <u>professional scientists</u> and <u>you</u>.

An Experiment Must be a Fair Test

1) One of the most important parts of planning an experiment is making sure that the <u>evidence</u> you collect is <u>valid</u> and <u>reliable</u> (see page 2). This means that your experiment must be a <u>fair test</u>.

2) The only way to make it a fair test is to <u>change</u> only <u>one variable</u> (factor) in the experiment. All the <u>other variables</u> should <u>be controlled</u> — they should <u>stay exactly the same</u> throughout the experiment and each time the experiment is repeated.

3) For example, if you're looking at the effect of <u>temperature</u> on the rate of an enzyme-controlled reaction you need to keep the <u>pH</u> the same each time (otherwise you won't know if any change in the rate of reaction is caused by the change in temperature, or the change in pH).

The Equipment Used Has to be Right for the Job

When you're planning an experiment, you need to make sure you choose the <u>right equipment</u>. For example, the measuring equipment you use has to be <u>sensitive enough</u> to accurately measure the chemicals you're using, e.g. if you need to measure out 11 ml of a liquid, you'll need to use a measuring cylinder that can measure to 1 ml, not 5 or 10 ml.

An Experiment Must be Safe

1) Part of planning an experiment is making sure that it's <u>safe</u>.

2) There are lots of <u>hazards</u> you could be faced with during an experiment, e.g. <u>microorganisms</u>, <u>chemicals</u>, <u>radiation</u>, <u>electricity</u>, <u>gas</u> and <u>fire</u>.

3) You should always make sure that you <u>identify</u> all the hazards that you might encounter.

4) You should also come up with ways of <u>reducing the risks</u> from the hazards you've identified.

5) One way of doing this is to carry out a <u>risk assessment</u>:

For an experiment involving a <u>Bunsen burner</u>, the risk assessment might be something like this:

<u>Hazard:</u> Bunsen burner is a fire risk.

<u>Precautions:</u>
- Keep flammable chemicals away from the Bunsen.
- Never leave the Bunsen unattended when lit.
- Always turn on the yellow safety flame when not in use.

Repeats affect Reliability, and Range of Measurements affects Validity

1) One way to make data <u>more reliable</u> is to <u>repeat</u> the measurements and take an <u>average</u> (see next page).

2) Also, the <u>range of data</u> collected has to be <u>suitable</u>, and you need to take <u>enough measurements</u> throughout the <u>whole</u> of the range — otherwise you won't be able to identify the <u>pattern</u> you're looking for. For example, if your hypothesis is that temperature affects the rate of an enzyme-controlled reaction, you'd need to measure the rate of reaction at a wide range of temperatures, e.g. 0 °C to 50 °C, and in 5 °C steps throughout the range.

3) If the range isn't big enough, or you don't take enough measurements throughout the range, your data <u>won't</u> be <u>valid</u> for the <u>hypothesis</u> you're supposed to be testing.

Take a look back at page 2 if you can't remember what reliability and validity are.

Reliable data — it won't ever forget your birthday...

All this stuff is really important — without <u>good quality</u> data an investigation will be totally <u>meaningless</u>. So give this page a read through a couple of times and your data will be the envy of the whole scientific community.

Collecting, Processing and Presenting Data

After you've collected your data you'll have <u>oodles of info</u> that you have to <u>make some kind of sense of</u>. You need to <u>process</u> and <u>present</u> it so you can look for <u>patterns</u> and <u>relationships</u> in it.

Data *Needs to be Organised*

1) <u>Tables</u> are dead useful for <u>recording results</u> and <u>organising data</u>.

2) When you draw a table, make sure that <u>each column</u> has a <u>heading</u> and that you've included the <u>units</u>.

3) Annoyingly, tables are about as useful as a chocolate teapot for showing <u>patterns</u> or <u>relationships</u> in data. You need to use some kind of graph for that (see below).

Check For *Mistakes Made* **When** *Collecting Data*

1) When you've collected all the results for an experiment, you should have a look to see if there are any results that <u>don't seem to fit</u> in with the rest.

2) Most results vary a bit, but any that are totally different are called <u>anomalous results</u>.

3) If you ever get any anomalous results, you should investigate them to try to <u>work out what happened</u>. If you can work out what happened (e.g. you measured something wrong) you can <u>ignore</u> them when processing and presenting your data.

Data **Can be** *Processed* **Using a Bit of** *Maths*

1) When you've done repeats of an experiment you should always calculate the <u>mean</u> (average). To do this <u>ADD TOGETHER</u> all the data values and <u>DIVIDE</u> by the total number of values in the sample.

2) You might also need to calculate the <u>range</u> (how spread out the data is). To do this find the <u>LARGEST</u> number and <u>SUBTRACT</u> the <u>SMALLEST</u> number from it. *Ignore anomalous results when calculating these.*

EXAMPLE:

Test tube	Repeat 1 (g)	Repeat 2 (g)	Repeat 3 (g)	Mean (g)	Range (g)
A	28	37	32	(28 + 37 + 32) ÷ 3 = 32.3	37 − 28 = 9
B	47	51	60	(47 + 51 + 60) ÷ 3 = 52.7	60 − 47 = 13
C	68	72	70	(68 + 72 + 70) ÷ 3 = 70.0	72 − 68 = 4

If Your Data Comes in *Categories,* **Present It in a** *Bar Chart*

1) If one of the variables is <u>categoric</u> (comes in distinct categories, e.g. blood types, metals) you should use a <u>bar chart</u> to display the data.

2) You can also use a bar chart if one of the variables is <u>discrete</u> (the data can only take whole values and there are no in-between ones, e.g. number of people is discrete because you can't have half a person).

3) There are some <u>golden rules</u> you need to follow for <u>drawing</u> bar charts:

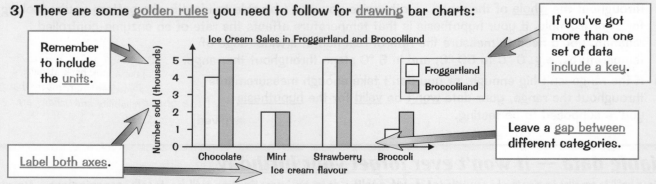

Remember to include the <u>units</u>.

If you've got more than one set of data <u>include a key</u>.

Ice Cream Sales in Froggartland and Broccoliland

Number sold (thousands)

Froggartland
Broccoliland

Chocolate Mint Strawberry Broccoli
Ice cream flavour

Leave a <u>gap between</u> different categories.

<u>Label both axes.</u>

Collecting, Processing and Presenting Data

If Your Data is Continuous, Plot a Line Graph

1) If both the variables are continuous (numerical data that can have any value within a range, e.g. length, volume, temperature) you should use a line graph to display the data.

2) Here are the rules for drawing line graphs:

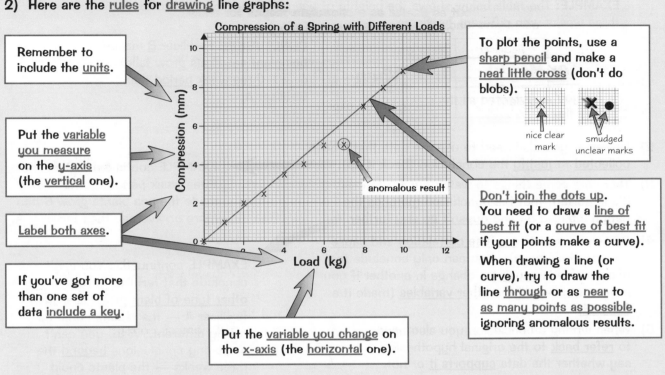

Remember to include the units.

Put the variable you measure on the y-axis (the vertical one).

Label both axes.

If you've got more than one set of data include a key.

Put the variable you change on the x-axis (the horizontal one).

Compression of a Spring with Different Loads

anomalous result

To plot the points, use a sharp pencil and make a neat little cross (don't do blobs).

nice clear mark

smudged unclear marks

Don't join the dots up. You need to draw a line of best fit (or a curve of best fit if your points make a curve).

When drawing a line (or curve), try to draw the line through or as near to as many points as possible, ignoring anomalous results.

Line Graphs Can Show Relationships in Data

1) Line graphs are used to show the relationship between two variables (just like other graphs).

2) Data can show three different types of correlation (relationship):

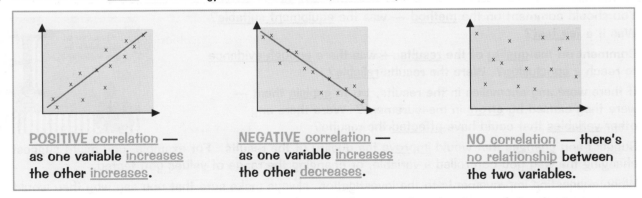

POSITIVE correlation — as one variable increases the other increases.

NEGATIVE correlation — as one variable increases the other decreases.

NO correlation — there's no relationship between the two variables.

3) You've got to be careful not to confuse correlation with cause though. A correlation just means that there's a relationship between two variables. It doesn't mean that the change in one variable is causing the change in the other (there might be other factors involved).

There's a positive correlation between age of man and length of nose hair...

Collect, process, present... data's like a difficult child — it needs a lot of attention. Go on, make it happy.

Drawing Conclusions and Evaluating

At the end of an experiment, the <u>conclusion</u> and <u>evaluation</u> are waiting. Don't worry, they won't bite.

You Can Only Conclude What the Data Shows and NO MORE

1) Drawing a conclusion can be quite straightforward — just <u>look at your data</u> and <u>say what pattern you see</u> between the variables.

EXAMPLE: The table below shows the heights of pea plant seedlings grown for three weeks with different fertilisers.

Fertiliser	Mean growth / mm
A	13.5
B	19.5
No fertiliser	5.5

<u>CONCLUSION</u>: Fertiliser <u>B</u> makes <u>pea plant</u> seedlings grow taller over a <u>three week period</u> than fertiliser A.

2) However, you also need to use the data that's been <u>collected</u> to <u>justify</u> the conclusion (back it up).

EXAMPLE continued... Over the three week period, Fertiliser B made the pea plants grow 6 mm more on average than fertiliser A.

3) There are some things to watch out for too — it's important that the conclusion <u>matches the data</u> it's based on and <u>doesn't go any further</u>.

4) Remember not to <u>confuse correlation</u> and <u>cause</u> (see previous page). You can only conclude that one variable is <u>causing</u> a change in another if you have controlled <u>all</u> the <u>other variables</u> (made it a <u>fair test</u>).

EXAMPLE continued... You can't conclude that fertiliser B makes <u>any other type of plant</u> grow taller than fertiliser A — the results could be totally different. Also, you can't make any conclusions <u>beyond</u> the three weeks — the plants could <u>drop dead</u>.

5) When writing a conclusion you also need to <u>refer back</u> to the original hypothesis — say whether the data <u>supports it</u> or not.

6) Then <u>explain</u> what's been found using your own <u>scientific knowledge</u> (what you've learnt in class).

Evaluation — Describe How You Could Improve the Investigation

1) You should comment on the <u>method</u> — was the <u>equipment suitable</u>? Was it a <u>fair test</u>?

2) Comment on the <u>quality</u> of the <u>results</u> — was there <u>enough evidence</u> to reach a <u>conclusion</u>? Were the results <u>reliable</u>?

I'd value this E somewhere in the region of 250-300k

3) If there were any anomalies in the results, try to <u>explain</u> them — were they caused by <u>errors</u> in measurement? Were there any other <u>variables</u> that could have <u>affected</u> the results?

4) Suggest any <u>changes</u> that would <u>improve</u> the quality of the results. For example, you might suggest changing the way you controlled a variable, or changing the range of values you tested.

5) When suggesting improvements to the investigation, always make sure that you say <u>why</u> they would make the results <u>better</u>.

Evaluation — next time, I will make sure I don't burn the lab down...

I know it doesn't seem very nice, but writing about where you went <u>wrong</u> is an important skill — it shows you've got a really good understanding of what the investigation was <u>about</u>. It's difficult for me — I'm always right.

How Science Works

The Controlled Assessment

You'll probably carry out a few investigations as you go through the course, but at some point you'll have to do the one that counts... the controlled assessment. Here's a bit about it...

The Controlled Assessment is Split into Three Parts

Part A — Planning

For this part you'll be given a hypothesis and asked to plan an experiment to test it. Write a method in a logical step-by-step order — you'll need to decide:

1) What variables you're going to control — and how you're going to control them.
2) What equipment to use — and say why you've chosen each bit of kit.
3) What risks are involved in the experiment — and say how you're going to reduce each of them.
4) The range of measurements you're going to take — and say why you've chosen that range.
5) How many times you'll repeat each measurement. You should do at least two repeats to make your data more reliable.

There's lots of help on all of these things on page 5.

You'll also need to say why your method is suitable for testing the hypothesis.

Part B — Observations

For Part B you'll be testing the hypothesis you were given in Part A by carrying out the experiment you planned. You'll need to:

1) Take an appropriate number and range of measurements (see page 5).
2) Repeat your measurements to get more reliable data (if possible) — two times is a good idea.
3) Record your data clearly in a nice, neat table (see page 6 for table tips).

Also, you'll need to find some secondary data (data collected by other people) that's relevant to the hypothesis. Make sure you say where you got the data from, and say how good quality the source was.

Part C — Conclusions

This part involves processing data, presenting data, drawing conclusions and evaluating. You'll have to do these things for your data (primary data), but also for the secondary data you collected in Part B. You'll need to:

1) Process all the data (both primary and secondary), e.g. calculate the mean (see page 6).
2) Present all the data using the right type of graph for each (see pages 6-7 for help with this).
3) Identify any anomalous results and explain why you didn't include them when you processed and presented your data (they'd reduce the validity of your results). If there aren't any anomalous results, then you need to say so.
4) Write conclusions that cover all the data (see previous page for what to say). Make sure you back up your conclusions using the data, say whether the conclusions support the hypothesis or not and explain what's been found using your own knowledge.
5) Write an evaluation (see previous page for what to include). Don't forget to say how the method affected the results, and how any improvements would make the results better.
6) Use your evaluation to say how confident you are in your conclusions. Think about other evidence that you could collect to give stronger support for your conclusions.

Keep your assessment under control — read this page...

Pretty straightforward, eh? As long as you've learnt everything on the previous few pages, you should be fine. Make sure you know each section like the back of your hand before you come to do the assessment itself.

How Science Works

Classification

It seems to be a basic human urge to want to classify things — that's the case in biology anyway...

Classification *is Organising Living Organisms into Groups*

1) Biologists classify organisms into groups based on how closely related they are to one another.

2) All living things are divided into five kingdoms — plants, animals, fungi, protoctists and prokaryotes.

3) Plants contain chlorophyll and are autotrophs (they're able to make their own food by photosynthesis). They're multicellular and have rigid cell walls, which support the cells.

4) Animals are heterotrophs — they can't make their own food, so they have to move about and find things to eat, e.g. plants. Animals are multicellular, like plants, but they don't have cell walls or chlorophyll.

5) Fungi are saprophytes — they feed off dead organisms and decaying material (nice). They're multicellular and have a cell wall, but don't have chlorophyll.

6) Protoctists are unicellular (single-celled) and have a nucleus, e.g. algae.

7) Prokaryotes are also unicellular but they don't have a nucleus, e.g. bacteria.

8) Sometimes it's hard to classify organisms. For example, most scientists think viruses are non-living, so they can't be placed in any kingdom.

9) Kingdoms are subdivided into smaller and smaller groups of organisms that have common features. →

> The phylum Chordata is made up of animals that all have a supporting rod-like structure that goes up the back of the body, e.g. this forms the backbone in vertebrates (see below).

Kingdom
Phylum
Class
Order
Family
Genus
Species

Etc

So a genus contains several species with similar features.

Animals *are Divided into Vertebrates and Invertebrates*

Vertebrates have a backbone and an internal skeleton — invertebrates don't (some have an external skeleton). Vertebrates are divided into five groups, called classes — fish, amphibians, reptiles, birds and mammals. Scientists divide vertebrates into these classes based on three main things:

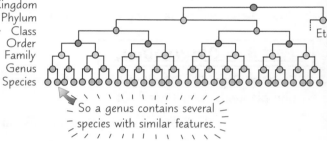

1) How they absorb OXYGEN — through lungs (e.g. birds), gills (e.g. fish) or skin (e.g. amphibians).

2) How they REPRODUCE — whether fertilisation occurs internally (e.g. mammals) or externally (e.g. fish). Also whether they are oviparous (lay eggs, e.g. reptiles) or viviparous (give birth to live young which are fed milk by the mother, e.g. mammals).

3) How they REGULATE THEIR INTERNAL BODY TEMPERATURE — whether they're homeotherms — this means they're 'warm-blooded' as their body temperature is kept constant by homeostasis, e.g. mammals. Or, whether they're poikilotherms — this means they're 'cold-blooded' as their body temperature changes with external temperature, e.g. reptiles.

The rules of the classification system were made up using the animals and plants that were known about at the time. Sometimes newly discovered species don't really fit into any of the categories.

E.g. the duck-billed platypus is an odd-looking thing, with a bill like a duck and a tail like a beaver. It's classed as a mammal because it has similar features to other mammals (e.g. it's homeothermic and suckles its young). BUT it lays eggs, whereas mammals usually give birth to live young. Hmm.

Talent shows are about organising singing organisms into groups...

Everything is grouped according to similarities and differences. The problem is that we make our groups based on the species we've already discovered — but when a new one turns up, it may not fit in very conveniently.

More on Classification

Classification isn't the most exciting thing ever (unlike doughnuts), but there's a bit more you need to know...

Accurate Classification isn't Always Easy...

Organisms are the same species if they can interbreed to produce fertile offspring. But sometimes
it's not easy to put organisms into nice neat boxes called species. Here are some examples why:

1) Not all organisms interbreed like the species definition says — some reproduce asexually but they're still
   the same species.

2) If a male from one species breeds with a female from a second species you'll get a hybrid and these can
   be fertile. E.g. many duck species interbreed to produce fertile hybrids (e.g. the Mallard with the
   Yellow-Billed Duck). This contradicts the species definition — according to it, all these ducks should be the
   same species. However, they're not because they're really different in many other ways, e.g. in genetics.

3) You'd expect members of the same species to look pretty similar. But there can be a lot of variation within
   a species. E.g. there are tons of breeds of dogs that look wildly different, but they're all the same species.

4) A ring species is a group of related populations that live in neighbouring areas.
   The populations that live next to each other can interbreed to produce fertile offspring,
   but populations that live further apart can't. An example is shown in the diagram.
   It's difficult to tell if all the populations are different species.

The Binomial System Gives Everything a Two-part Name

1) In the binomial system, each species is given a two-part Latin
   name. The first part refers to the genus that the organism
   belongs to and the second part refers to the species.

   > E.g. Humans are known as *Homo sapiens*.
   > '*Homo*' is the genus that they belong to
   > and '*sapiens*' is the species.

2) The binomial system has helped scientists to:

   - Identify species — it avoids confusion where common names mean different things in different places.
   - Study species — by identifying and naming species, scientists can share information on them.
   - Conserve species (especially endangered species) — e.g. it's easy to presume that two similar-looking
     organisms are the same species, when they're actually different. This could mean that only one
     species is protected, whilst the other becomes extinct.
   - Target conservation efforts — we can protect areas that have a great variety of different species,
     e.g. tropical rainforests, to prevent a huge number of species being destroyed.

Keys are Used to Identify Creatures

1) A key is a series of questions that you can use to figure out what an unknown organism is.

2) You start at question 1, and the answer to that question (which you know by looking at your mystery
   organism) is used to narrow down your options of what it could be.

3) As you answer more and more questions you narrow down your options further until eventually you're
   just left with one possible species your organism could be.

   Example: A student saw the following living things in a pond.
   Using the key provided, work out what each organism is.

1)	Can the organism produce its own food? ....YES, then it's a water lily ....NO — go to question 2
2)	Does the organism have six legs? ....YES, then it's a dragonfly ....NO — go to question 3
3)	Does the organism have gills? ....YES, then it's a fish ....NO, then it's a frog

Binomial system — uh oh, sounds like maths...

You might have to construct a key in an exam. The easiest way is to make each question identify one organism.
E.g. if the list of organisms include a bird, you could ask "does the organism have feathers?" to identify it.

Variation

You'll probably have noticed that not all people are identical. There are reasons for this.

Organisms of the Same Species Have Differences

1) Different species look... well... different — my dog definitely doesn't look like a daisy.

2) But even organisms of the <u>same species</u> will usually look at least <u>slightly</u> different — e.g. in a room full of people you'll see different <u>colour hair</u>, individually <u>shaped noses</u>, a variety of <u>heights</u> etc.

3) These differences are called the <u>variation</u> within a species — and there are <u>two</u> causes of variation: <u>genes</u> and the <u>environment</u>.

Different Genes Cause Genetic Variation

1) All plants and animals have <u>characteristics</u> that are in some ways similar to their <u>parents'</u> (e.g. I've got my dad's nose, apparently).

2) This is because an organism's <u>characteristics</u> are determined by the <u>genes inherited</u> from their <u>parents</u>. (Genes are the <u>codes</u> inside your cells that <u>control</u> how you're made — more about these on page 16.)

3) Most animals (and quite a lot of plants) get <u>some</u> genes from the <u>mother</u> and <u>some</u> from the <u>father</u>.

4) This combining of genes from two parents causes <u>genetic variation</u> — no two of the species are <u>genetically identical</u> (other than identical twins).

5) Genetic variation also occurs due to <u>mutations</u> — <u>changes</u> in an organism's <u>genes</u>. These changes can cause differences in an organism's <u>characteristics</u>.

6) <u>Some</u> characteristics are determined <u>only</u> by genes (e.g. violet flower colour). In <u>animals</u> these include: <u>eye colour</u>, <u>blood group</u> and <u>inherited disorders</u> (e.g. haemophilia or cystic fibrosis).

Characteristics are also Influenced by the Environment

1) The <u>environment</u> that organisms <u>live and grow</u> in also causes <u>differences</u> between members of the same species — this is called <u>environmental variation</u>.

2) Environmental variation covers a <u>wide range</u> of differences — from <u>losing your toes</u> in a piranha attack, to getting a <u>suntan</u>, to having <u>yellow leaves</u> (never happened to me yet though), and so on.

3) <u>Environmental factors</u> that can cause variation include <u>diet</u>, <u>exercise</u>, <u>temperature</u>, <u>light level</u>, <u>amount of water</u> etc.

A plant grown on a nice sunny windowsill would grow <u>luscious</u> and <u>green</u>.

The same plant grown in darkness would grow <u>tall and spindly</u> and its leaves would turn <u>yellow</u> — these are <u>environmental variations</u>.

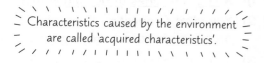

Characteristics caused by the environment are called 'acquired characteristics'.

Most Characteristics are Due to Genes AND the Environment

1) <u>Most characteristics</u> (e.g. body weight, height, skin colour, condition of teeth, academic or athletic prowess, etc.) are determined by a <u>mixture</u> of <u>genetic</u> and <u>environmental</u> factors.

2) For example, the <u>maximum height</u> that an animal or plant could grow to is determined by its <u>genes</u>. But whether it actually grows that tall depends on its <u>environment</u> (e.g. how much food it gets).

My mum's got no trousers — cos I've got her jeans...

So, you are the way you are partly because of the genes you inherited off your folks. But you can't blame it <u>all</u> on your parents, since your <u>environment</u> then takes over and begins to mould you in all sorts of ways. In fact, it's often really tricky to decide which factor is <u>more influential</u>, your genes or the environment.

Continuous and Discontinuous Variation

I'm afraid you're not finished with variation yet — you need to know about the difference between <u>continuous</u> and <u>discontinuous</u> variation. It's not too complicated, honest...

Variation can be Continuous...

<u>Continuous variation</u> is when the individuals in a population <u>vary within a range</u> — there are <u>no distinct categories</u>, e.g. humans can be any height within a range (139 cm, 175 cm, 185.9 cm...), not just tall or short. Here are some more examples:

- <u>Animals</u> — e.g. <u>humans</u> can be any <u>mass</u> within a range.
- <u>Microorganisms</u> — e.g. the <u>width</u> of <u>E. coli</u> bacteria varies within a range.
- <u>Plants</u> — e.g. a <u>tree</u> can have any <u>number of leaves</u> within a range.

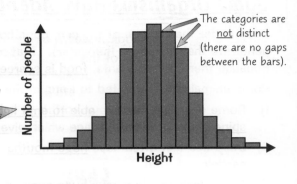

The categories are <u>not</u> distinct (there are no gaps between the bars).

A graph of continuous variation is an example of a <u>normal distribution curve</u> (a bell-shaped curve).

This isn't too scary — it just means that if you draw a <u>line graph</u> of your data you get a nice <u>symmetrical</u> curve. Here's that height example again:

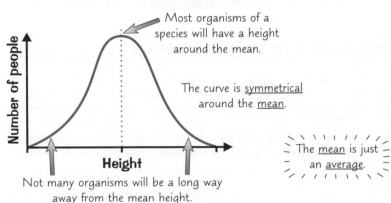

Most organisms of a species will have a height around the mean.

The curve is <u>symmetrical</u> around the <u>mean</u>.

The <u>mean</u> is just an <u>average</u>.

Not many organisms will be a long way away from the mean height.

...or Discontinuous

<u>Discontinuous variation</u> is when there are <u>two or more distinct categories</u> — each individual falls into <u>only one</u> of these categories, there are <u>no intermediates</u>. Here are some examples:

- <u>Animals</u> — e.g. <u>humans</u> can only be <u>blood group</u> A, B, AB or O.
- <u>Microorganisms</u> — e.g. <u>bacteria</u> are either <u>antibiotic-resistant</u> or not.
- <u>Plants</u> — e.g. the <u>colour</u> of a <u>courgette</u> is either yellow, dark green or light green.

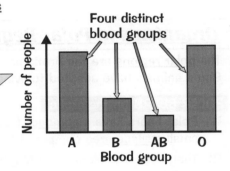

Four distinct blood groups

You Can Do a Practical to Show Variation

<u>Continuous</u> and <u>discontinuous</u> variation is easy to investigate in a group of people e.g. <u>your class</u>.

Continuous Variation

Record the <u>hand span</u> of everyone in your class (to find it, spread out your hand and measure the distance from the tip of the little finger to the tip of the thumb). You'll get a <u>range of data</u>, so you can draw a graph like the blue one above.

Discontinuous Variation

Record the <u>eye colour</u> of everyone in your class. You'll get data in <u>distinct categories</u> such as blue, brown etc. So you can draw a graph like the red one above.

My favourite blood group is AB B A...*

If you can't remember the difference between continuous and discontinuous just think of test results — e.g. if some results vary from 0% to 65.4% to 100% and anything in between, then they're <u>continuous</u>. But if some results are just pass or fail, they're <u>discontinuous</u>. Hope that helps you to pass your tests.

*Ask your mum.

Extreme Environments

Organisms which live in extreme environments like deserts or deep oceans need to be specially adapted.

Some Organisms Have Adapted to Living in the Deep Sea

Deep under the surface of the sea, conditions are hard to live in. There's virtually no light (sunlight can't penetrate that deep into the water). That means plants can't grow because they can't photosynthesise. Because there are no plants, food is scarce — organisms survive on scraps that sink down from above.

Some animals have adapted to living in the deep ocean, e.g.

1) Some deep-sea fish are able to emit light from parts of their body. E.g. the angler fish has a rod-shaped spine sticking out of its face which gives out light. The light attracts prey, which the angler fish then eats.

2) Deep-sea fish often have huge mouths, e.g. the rat-tail fish which moves along the seabed scooping up particles of food.

3) Many deep-sea fish have huge eyes adapted to the dark, and long feelers to help them locate prey.

Organisms in Volcanic Vents are Adapted to High Temperatures

There are volcanic vents in the seabed that send out hot water and minerals into the cold ocean. Some organisms have adapted to living around them.

Volcanic vents are also called hydrothermal vents.

1) The chemicals from the vents support bacteria that are able to make their own food using chemical energy. This is called chemosynthesis. It's a bit like photosynthesis, but (because there's hardly any light down there) it uses chemical energy instead of light energy.

2) These bacteria are at the bottom of a food web (they're producers) — animals feed on the bacteria.

3) The conditions are extremely hot and under high pressure. The bacteria which live near the vents must be specially adapted to cope with the high temperature and pressure.

Organisms in Polar Regions Have Adapted to the Cold

The polar regions are the Arctic and Antarctic — these places are really cold. Some animals have adapted to living in these conditions e.g:

POLAR BEARS (in the arctic)

1) Polar bears have a compact (rounded) shape, which gives them a small surface area compared to volume — this reduces heat loss.

2) They have a thick layer of blubber for insulation — this also acts as an energy store when food is scarce.

3) Their thick hairy coats trap a layer of warm air next to the skin, and their greasy fur sheds water (this prevents cooling due to evaporation).

4) Their big feet help by spreading their weight — which stops them sinking into the snow or breaking thin ice.

5) Polar bears have white fur to match their surroundings — for camouflage.

PENGUINS (in the antarctic)

1) Penguins have similar adaptations to polar bears, such as a thick layer of insulating fat and oily feathers to shed water, which reduce heat loss.

2) They also huddle together in groups to conserve heat.

3) Penguins have a streamlined body to reduce water resistance — so they can swim fast to catch fish.

Zebras — adapted for hiding in front of railings...

You could go to the most horrible, dry, desolate, smelly, freezing, airless place in the world, and there would still be some well-adapted little critter able to live there. Take my house for example — it's freezing since the boiler broke, but I've adapted (if an extra jumper counts).

Natural Selection and Evidence for Evolution

There are always more organisms born than can survive, so they end up <u>competing</u> for stuff like food.
Only the <u>fittest</u> survive, and they will <u>pass on</u> their characteristics to their offspring.

Natural Selection Means "Survival of the Fittest"

<u>Evolution</u> is the <u>slow and continuous change</u> of organisms from one generation to the next.
<u>Charles Darwin</u> came up with the <u>theory of natural selection</u> to <u>explain how</u> evolution occurs. It works like this:

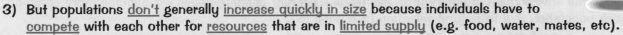

1) Individuals are not all the same because of differences in their genes.
   So there is <u>variation</u> (see page 12) within populations of organisms.
2) Most organisms give birth to <u>more young</u> than can <u>survive</u> to adulthood.
3) But populations <u>don't</u> generally <u>increase quickly in size</u> because individuals have to
   <u>compete</u> with each other for <u>resources</u> that are in <u>limited supply</u> (e.g. food, water, mates, etc).
4) Those individuals with characteristics that make them <u>better adapted</u> to the environment
   have a <u>better chance of survival</u> and so are more likely to <u>breed</u> successfully.
5) So, the <u>genes</u> that are responsible for the useful characteristics are more likely to be <u>passed on</u>
   to the <u>next generation</u>.
6) However, some individuals will be <u>less well adapted</u> to their environment and may be less able
   to compete. These individuals are <u>less likely</u> to survive and reproduce.
7) <u>Over time</u>, there will be a higher proportion of individuals with <u>beneficial characteristics</u> — compared to
   those with <u>poorly adapted characteristics</u>. Eventually the poorly adapted characteristics may be <u>lost</u>.

There's Evidence to Support Evolution:

1 DNA Research

1) The theory of evolution suggests that all organisms
   have evolved from <u>shared common ancestors</u>.
2) Closely related species <u>diverged</u> (evolved to
   become different species) more <u>recently</u>.
3) Evolution is caused by <u>gradual changes</u> in DNA.
4) So, organisms that diverged away from each other more
   <u>recently</u> should have more <u>similar DNA</u>. This is exactly what
   scientists found, e.g. <u>humans</u> and <u>chimps</u> have similar DNA.

2 Resistant Organisms

1) The poison <u>warfarin</u>
   was used to <u>kill rats</u>.
2) But a certain gene gives
   rats <u>resistance</u> to warfarin
   — these rats are more likely
   to <u>survive</u> and <u>breed</u>.
3) So now there are rat populations
   that are <u>warfarin-resistant</u>.

The Scientific Community Validates Evidence About Evolution

1) The <u>scientific community</u> is all the scientists around the world, e.g. researchers, technicians and professors.
2) Scientists within the scientific community <u>accept</u> the theory of evolution because they've <u>shared</u> and
   <u>discussed</u> the <u>evidence</u> to make sure it's <u>valid</u> and <u>reliable</u>. There are three main ways they do this:

Scientists publish their work in <u>SCIENTIFIC JOURNALS</u>
(academic magazines). If other scientists can repeat
the experiments using the same methods and get the
<u>same results</u>, the scientific community can be pretty
confident that the evidence is <u>reliable</u>.

Before scientists can publish their work it has
to undergo <u>PEER REVIEW</u>. This is when other
scientists (peers) read and review the work,
to check it's <u>valid</u> and that experiments are
carried out to the <u>highest possible standards</u>.

<u>SCIENTIFIC CONFERENCES</u> are <u>meetings</u> that scientists attend to <u>present</u> and <u>discuss</u> their
work. They're an easy way for the latest hypotheses and evidence to be <u>shared</u> and <u>discussed</u>.

Natural selection... sounds like vegan chocolates...

Natural selection's all about the organisms with the <u>best characteristics</u> surviving to <u>pass on their genes</u>
so that the whole species ends up <u>adapted</u> to its environment. It doesn't happen overnight though.

Speciation and Genes

First up, speciation — where evolution can lead to new species. Then you need to get to grips with genes...

Speciation is the Development of a New Species

Speciation occurs when populations of the same species become so different that they can no longer breed together to produce fertile offspring. It works like this:

1. Isolation is where populations of a species are separated. This can happen due to a physical barrier. E.g. floods and earthquakes can cause barriers that geographically isolate some individuals from the main population.

2. Conditions on either side of the barrier will be slightly different, e.g. they may have different climates. Because the environment is different on each side, different characteristics will become more common in each population due to natural selection (see page 15).

3. Eventually, individuals from the different populations will have changed so much that they won't be able to breed with one another to produce fertile offspring. The two groups will have become separate species.

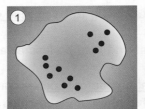 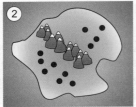  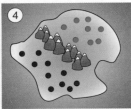

Two populations of the same species
● = individual organism
⟹ Physical barriers separate populations.
⟹ Populations adapt to new environments.
⟹ Development of a new species.

You Need to Know All About Genes...

DNA molecule

Most cells in your body have a nucleus. The nucleus contains your genetic material in the form of chromosomes.

nucleus

The human cell nucleus contains 23 pairs of chromosomes. There are two No. 19 chromosomes, two No. 12s, etc.

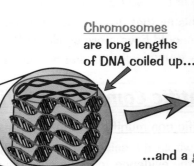

Chromosomes are long lengths of DNA coiled up...

...and a gene is a short section of this DNA.

Chromosomes carry genes. Different genes control the development of different characteristics, e.g. hair colour.

There can be different versions of the same gene, which give different versions of a characteristic, like blue or brown eyes. The different versions of the same gene are called alleles. Since there are two copies of each chromosome, there are two copies of each gene — so you might have two alleles the same or two different alleles (see the next page).

Genes — they always come in pairs...

Genes are important because they control everything a cell does, as well as what characteristics are passed on. Make sure you really know your stuff 'cos you're going to hear a lot more about genes over the next few pages...

Genetic Diagrams

In genetics you're never more than a stone's throw away from a genetic diagram...

Genetic Diagrams Show the Possible Genes of Offspring

First of all, make sure you remember what an allele is from the previous page.
Then you need to learn these basics (otherwise it's hard to follow what's going on).

Remember, gametes (sperm or egg cells) only have one allele, but all the other cells in an organism have two.

1) In genetic diagrams letters are usually used to represent alleles.

2) If an organism has two alleles for a particular gene the same, then it's homozygous.
If its two alleles for a particular gene are different, then it's heterozygous.

3) If the two alleles are different, only one can determine what characteristic is present. The allele for the characteristic that's shown is called the dominant allele (use a capital letter for dominant alleles — e.g. 'C'). The other one is called recessive (and you show these with small letters — e.g. 'c').

4) For an organism to display a recessive characteristic, both its alleles must be recessive (e.g. cc). But to display a dominant characteristic the organism can be either CC or Cc, because the dominant allele overrules the recessive one if the plant/animal/other organism is heterozygous.

Suppose You Find Yourself Cross-Breeding Crazy Hamsters...

Let's say that the gene which causes the crazy nature is recessive, so we use a small "h" for it, whilst normal (boring) behaviour is due to a dominant gene, so we represent it with a capital "H".

1) A crazy hamster must have the genotype hh. However, a normal hamster could have two possible genotypes — HH or Hh.

Genotype means what alleles you have. Phenotype means the actual characteristic.

2) Here's what happens if you breed from two homozygous hamsters:

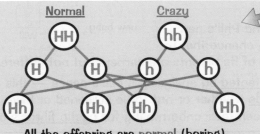

If you don't like that diagram you can also do it like this:

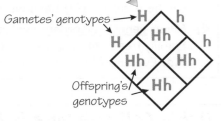

3) If two of these offspring now breed, you'll get the next generation:

When you cross two parents to look at just one characteristic, it's called a monohybrid cross.

4) This gives a 3:1 ratio of normal to crazy offspring in this generation.
Remember that "results" like this are only probabilities — they don't say definitely what'll happen.
(most likely, you'll end up trying to contain a mini-riot of nine lunatic baby hamsters.)

What do you get if you cross a kangaroo and a sheep...

...a ratio of 1:1 kangsheep to sheeparoos... bet you thought I was going to say a woolly jumper.
In the exam you might be given the results of a breeding experiment and asked to say whether a characteristic is dominant or recessive. To figure it out, look at the ratios of the characteristic in different generations — just like in the diagrams. And remember that a 3:1 ratio of normal:crazy gives a 1 in 4 or 25% probability of being crazy.

Genetic Diagrams and Disorders

Usually we don't notice our genes — they all quietly bumble away, making proteins.
But a <u>faulty allele</u> (that makes a faulty protein) can cause a <u>genetic disorder</u>.

Cystic Fibrosis is Caused by a Recessive Allele

Cystic fibrosis is a <u>genetic disorder</u> of the <u>cell membranes</u>. It <u>results</u> in the body producing a lot of thick sticky <u>mucus</u> in the <u>air passages</u>, <u>gut</u> and <u>pancreas</u>. Symptoms include <u>breathing difficulties</u>, <u>lung infections</u>, <u>malnutrition</u> and <u>fertility problems</u>.

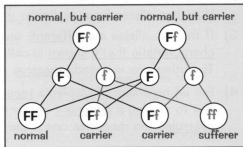

1) The allele which causes cystic fibrosis is a <u>recessive allele</u>, 'f', carried by about <u>1 person in 30</u>.

2) Because it's recessive, people with only <u>one copy</u> of the allele <u>won't</u> have the disorder — they're known as <u>carriers</u>.

3) For a child to have a chance of inheriting the disorder, <u>both parents</u> must be either <u>carriers</u> or <u>sufferers</u>.

4) As the diagram shows there's a <u>1 in 4 chance</u> of a child having the disorder if <u>both</u> parents are <u>carriers</u>.

Knowing how inheritance works can help you to interpret a <u>family tree</u> (sometimes called a <u>pedigree</u>) — this is one for <u>cystic fibrosis</u>.

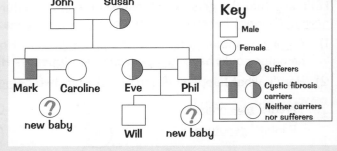

1) From the family tree, you can tell that the allele for cystic fibrosis <u>isn't</u> dominant because plenty of the family <u>carry</u> the allele but <u>aren't sufferers</u>.

2) There is a <u>0%</u> chance that Mark and Caroline's new baby will be a sufferer (ff) because Caroline is normal (FF).

3) There is a <u>25%</u> chance that Eve and Phil's new baby will be a sufferer and a <u>50%</u> chance that it will be a carrier (Ff) because both of its parents are carriers but not sufferers.

4) Many <u>genetic disorders</u> can be <u>detected</u> by analysing a cell's <u>genes</u> — this is <u>screening</u>. Family trees can help people <u>decide</u> whether or not to be screened or have their unborn baby screened. E.g. Eve and Phil may want to screen their unborn baby for <u>cystic fibrosis</u> because they're both carriers.

Sickle Cell Anaemia is Also Caused by a Recessive Allele

1) Sickle-cell anaemia is a <u>genetic disorder</u> characterised by funny-shaped red blood cells.

2) These red blood cells can get <u>stuck</u> in the capillaries, which <u>deprives</u> body cells of <u>oxygen</u>.

3) <u>Symptoms</u> include tiredness, painful joints and muscles, fever and anaemia.

4) It's caused by inheriting two <u>recessive</u> alleles 'a' (for anaemia). The normal allele is represented by an 'A'.

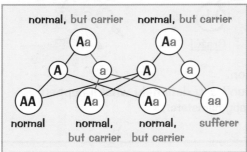

- If two people who <u>carry</u> the sickle cell anaemia allele have children, the <u>probability</u> of each child suffering from the disorder is 1 in 4 — <u>25%</u>.

- The ratio you'd expect in the children is <u>3:1</u>, non-sufferer:sufferer.

- If you see this ratio in the offspring you know <u>both</u> parents must have the <u>two different alleles</u>.

- Be careful with this one — it may be disguised as a <u>1:2:1</u> ratio (normal:carrier:sufferer), but it means the same thing.

Unintentional mooning — caused by faulty jeans...

We <u>all</u> have defective genes in us somewhere — but usually they don't cause a problem (as they're often <u>recessive</u>, and so if you have a healthy <u>dominant</u> allele too, you'll be fine).

Revision Summary for B1 Topic 1

Gee, all that business about all those topics — and it's all pretty serious stuff. It takes a real effort to get your head round it all. There are too many big fancy words, for one thing. But there you go — life's tough and you've just gotta face up to it. Use these questions to find out what you know — and what you don't. Then look back and learn the bits you didn't know. Then try the questions again, and again...

1) Briefly describe characteristics of organisms in the animal kingdom.
2) What main characteristic do organisms in the Chordata phylum have in common?
3) What do all vertebrates have in common?
4) What does oviparous mean? Name a group of vertebrates that are oviparous.
5) What is a species?
6) What is the name for the offspring of two different species?
7) In the binomial system each organism is given a two-part name. What does each part refer to?
8)* Devise a key to tell apart a worm, a snail, a centipede and a spider.
9) Other than the environment, what causes variation?
10) List three features of animals which aren't affected at all by environment, and three which are.
11) What is: a) continuous variation?
             b) discontinuous variation?
12) Give an example of a feature in humans where there is: a) continuous variation.
                                                            b) discontinuous variation.
13) Explain two ways that deep-sea fish have adapted to their habitat.
14) Explain two ways that polar bears are adapted to living in polar regions.
15) Explain Darwin's theory of natural selection.
16) Give three ways that the scientific community validate evidence.
17) What is speciation? Explain how geographical isolation can lead to speciation.
18) Draw a set of diagrams showing the relationship between: cell, nucleus, chromosomes, genes, DNA.
19) How many pairs of chromosomes are there in a normal human cell nucleus?
20) What is an allele?
21) What is meant by an organism being heterozygous? What about homozygous?
22) Describe the basic difference between a recessive allele and a dominant one.
23)*White colour in a plant is carried on a recessive allele, b. The dominant allele, B, gives blue flowers. After a cross between two plants, all the flowers of the second generation are blue. These are bred together and the result in the third generation is a ratio of 54 blue : 19 white flowers. What were the alleles of the flowers in the first generation?
24) What are the symptoms of cystic fibrosis?
25) Cystic fibrosis is caused by a recessive allele.
    If both parents are carriers, what is the probability of their child: a) being a carrier?
                                                                          b) suffering from the disorder?
26) Give two symptoms of sickle-cell anaemia.
27) Is the allele for sickle-cell anaemia dominant or recessive?

*Answers to these questions are given on p.108

Homeostasis

Homeostasis means <u>maintaining</u> the right <u>conditions</u> inside your body, so that everything <u>works properly</u>. Ace.

Homeostasis **is Maintaining a** *Stable Internal Environment*

Conditions in your body need to be kept <u>steady</u> so that cells can function properly. For example...

1) <u>Osmoregulation</u> (regulating <u>water</u> content) — you need to keep a balance between the water you gain (in drink, food, and from respiration) and the water you pee, sweat and breathe out.

2) <u>Thermoregulation</u> (regulating <u>body temperature</u>) — you need to get rid of <u>excess</u> body heat when you're hot, but <u>retain</u> heat when the environment is cold. See below for how your body does this.

3) <u>Blood glucose</u> regulation — you need to keep the glucose in your blood at a <u>steady level</u> (see p.24).

A mechanism called <u>negative feedback</u> helps to keep all these things steady:

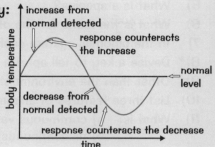

increase from normal detected
response counteracts the increase
normal level
decrease from normal detected
response counteracts the decrease
time
body temperature

*   Changes in the environment trigger a response that <u>counteracts</u> the changes — e.g. a <u>rise</u> in body temperature causes a response that <u>lowers body temperature</u>.

*   This means that the <u>internal environment</u> tends to stay around a <u>norm</u>, the level at which the cells work best.

*   This only works within <u>certain limits</u> — if the environment changes too much then it might not be possible to <u>counteract</u> it.

Body Temperature **is Controlled by the** *Hypothalamus*

All <u>enzymes</u> work best at a <u>certain temperature</u>. The enzymes in the human body work best at about <u>37 °C</u>.

1) There's a part of your brain called the <u>hypothalamus</u> that acts as your own <u>personal thermostat</u>.

2) It contains <u>receptors</u> that are sensitive to the <u>blood temperature</u> in the brain. It also receives impulses from receptors in the <u>skin</u> (nerve endings) that provide information about <u>skin temperature</u>.

3) When the hypothalamus detects a change, it causes a <u>response</u> in the <u>dermis</u> (deep layer of the skin):

When temperature receptors detect you're TOO HOT:

1) <u>Erector muscles</u> relax, so <u>hairs</u> lie flat.

2) <u>Lots of sweat</u> (containing <u>water</u> and <u>salts</u>) is produced. When the sweat <u>evaporates</u> it <u>transfers heat</u> from your skin to the environment, cooling you down.

3) <u>Blood vessels</u> close to the surface of the skin <u>dilate</u> (widen). This is called <u>vasodilation</u>. It allows <u>more blood</u> to flow near the <u>surface</u>, so it can <u>transfer more heat</u> into the <u>surroundings</u>.

And when they detect you're TOO COLD:

1) <u>Erector muscles</u> contract. <u>Hairs</u> stand on end to trap an insulating layer of air, which helps keep you warm.

2) <u>Very little sweat</u> is produced.

3) Blood vessels near the surface of the skin constrict (<u>vasoconstriction</u>). This means <u>less blood</u> flows near the surface, so <u>less heat</u> is transferred to the surroundings.

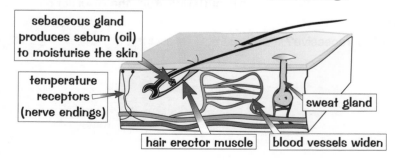

sebaceous gland produces sebum (oil) to moisturise the skin

temperature receptors (nerve endings)

sweat gland

hair erector muscle

blood vessels widen

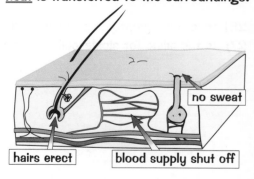

no sweat

hairs erect

blood supply shut off

Learn about homeostasis — and keep your cool...

<u>Homeostasis</u> means 'maintaining a <u>stable internal environment</u>'. Say this 20 times and recite it in your sleep. As well as keeping your <u>temperature</u> right, it's also about keeping <u>water</u> and <u>sugar</u> at the right level. Lovely jubbly.

Hormones and Nerves

There are two ways that signals can be sent from one part of the body to another — using slooow <u>hormones</u> or quick quick quick <u>nerves</u>. And guess what, you have to know about them <u>both</u>. Enjoy. You're welcome.

Hormones <u>are</u> Chemical Messengers <u>Sent in the</u> Blood

1) Hormones are chemicals produced in various <u>glands</u> (called <u>endocrine</u> glands).

2) They are released directly into the <u>blood</u>. The blood then carries them to other parts of the body.

3) They travel all over the body but they only affect <u>particular cells</u> in particular places.

4) The affected cells are called <u>target cells</u> — they have the right <u>receptors</u> to respond to that hormone. An organ that contains target cells is called a <u>target organ</u>.

5) Hormones travel at "<u>the speed of blood</u>".

6) They have <u>long-lasting effects</u>.

> **Learn this definition:**
> Hormones ...are <u>chemical</u> <u>messengers</u> which <u>travel in the</u> <u>blood</u> to <u>activate target cells</u>.

Neurones <u>Transmit Information Around the Body</u>

<u>Neurones</u> (nerve cells) transmit information as <u>electrical impulses</u> around the body.

1) Neurones have <u>branched endings</u> called <u>dendrons</u>, so they can <u>connect</u> with lots of other neurones.

2) The electrical impulse is passed along the <u>axon</u> of the cell.

3) There's a <u>myelin sheath</u> along the axon that acts as an <u>electrical insulator</u>, which stops the impulse getting <u>lost</u>. It also <u>speeds</u> up the electrical impulse.

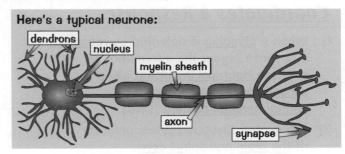

Here's a typical neurone:
dendrons
nucleus
myelin sheath
axon
synapse

4) Neurones are <u>long</u>, which also <u>speeds up</u> the impulse (<u>connecting</u> with <u>another neurone</u> slows the impulse down, so one long neurone is much <u>quicker</u> than lots of short ones joined together).

5) The <u>connection</u> between <u>two neurones</u> is called a <u>synapse</u>. It's basically just a very tiny gap:

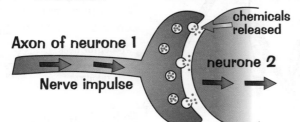

Axon of neurone 1
chemicals released
neurone 2
Nerve impulse

- The nerve impulse is transmitted by chemicals called <u>neurotransmitters</u>, which <u>diffuse</u> across the gap.

- The neurotransmitters then set off a <u>new electrical impulse</u> in the <u>next neurone</u>.

Hormones <u>and</u> Nerves <u>Do Similar Jobs — but There are</u> Differences

Nerves	1) Very <u>FAST</u> message.
	2) Act for a very <u>SHORT TIME</u>.
	3) Act on a very <u>PRECISE AREA</u>.
	4) <u>ELECTRICAL</u> message.

Hormones	1) <u>SLOWER</u> message.
	2) Act for a <u>LONG TIME</u>.
	3) Act in a more <u>GENERAL</u> way.
	4) <u>CHEMICAL</u> message.

Laughing at a funny joke releases stress-relieving hormones...

What's red and sits in the corner... A naughty strawberry. So now you're fully destressed, listen up... Hormones control various <u>organs</u> and <u>cells</u> in the body, though they tend to control things that aren't <u>immediately</u> life-threatening. They're not as quick as using neurones, but their effects can last much <u>longer</u>.

The Nervous System

The nervous system is what lets you react to what goes on around you, so you'd find life tough without it.

Sense Organs Detect Stimuli

A stimulus is a change in your environment that you may need to react to (e.g. a grizzly bear looking hungrily at you). You need to be constantly monitoring what's going on so you can respond if you need to.

1) You have five different sense organs — eyes, ears, nose, tongue and skin.

2) They all contain different receptors. Receptors are groups of cells which are sensitive to a stimulus. They change stimulus energy (e.g. light energy) into electrical impulses.

3) A stimulus can be light, sound, touch, pressure, chemical, or a change in position or temperature.

The Central Nervous System Coordinates a Response

1) When a stimulus is detected by receptors in a sense organ, the information is sent (as electrical impulses) along sensory neurones to the central nervous system (CNS).

2) The central nervous system consists of the brain and spinal cord.

3) The CNS coordinates the response (in other words, it decides what to do about the stimulus and tells something to do it).

4) The CNS then sends information to an effector (muscle or gland) along a motor neurone. The effector then responds accordingly.

The Five Sense Organs and the receptors that each contains:

1) Eyes — Light receptors.

2) Ears — Sound and "balance" receptors.

3) Nose — Smell receptors — sensitive to chemical stimuli.

4) Tongue — Taste receptors — sensitive to bitter, salt, sweet, sour and savoury (these are all chemical stimuli)

5) Skin — Sensitive to touch (pressure) and temperature change.

Sensory Neurones

Long dendrons and short axons carry nerve impulses from the receptors in the sense organs to the CNS.

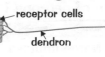
receptor cells / dendron / axon

Relay Neurones

Many short dendrons and axons carry nerve impulses from sensory neurones to motor neurones.

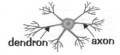
dendron / axon

Effectors

Muscles and glands are known as effectors — they respond in different ways. Muscles contract in response to a nervous impulse, whereas glands secrete substances, e.g. hormones.

The function of axons and dendrons is covered on page 21.

Motor Neurones

Many short dendrons and one long axon carry nerve impulses from the CNS to the effectors (muscle or gland).

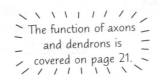

dendron / axon / effector cells

Your tongue's evolved for Chinese meals — sweet, sour, MSG...

I'm so kind, I've just spent a whole hour thinking of how you could remember the order of a coordinated response: stimulus, receptor, sensory neurone, CNS, motor neurone, effector, response. Ready? Sofa, remote, search for Neighbours, choose 'Neighbours series', mental note when it's on, easy — record it.

Investigating Stimuli and Reflexes

If you were to unfold your brain and lie it out flat, it would cover an ironing board. Apparently.*

You can Carry Out a Practical to Investigate External Stimuli

For example, you can investigate skin sensitivity like this:

1) In pairs, one person wears a blindfold, or promises not to look.

2) The other person uses a hairpin (or a paperclip) with the 2 points a fixed distance apart (e.g. start at 3 mm) to touch an area of the blindfolded person's skin (e.g their elbow).

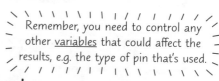

3) The blindfolded person is then asked how many points they can feel.

4) If the blindfolded person only feels one point, the experiment is repeated with the points further apart until they feel two points. The distance at which they feel two points is recorded.

5) This is repeated for different areas of skin (e.g. toes, fingers).

6) On really sensitive places, like the fingers or lips, the blindfolded person will feel both points when they're a short distance apart. This is because sensitive areas have lots of touch receptors.

Remember, you need to control any other variables that could affect the results, e.g. the type of pin that's used.

7) But on less sensitive areas, like the elbow, they'll only feel both points when they're much further apart, because these areas have fewer touch receptors.

Reflexes Help Prevent Injury

1) Reflexes are automatic responses to certain stimuli — they can reduce the chances of being injured.

2) For example, if someone shines a bright light in your eyes, your pupils automatically get smaller so that less light gets into the eye — this stops it getting damaged.

3) The passage of information in a reflex (from receptor to effector) is called a reflex arc.

A Reflex Arc Goes Through the Central Nervous System

5. Message travels along a motor neurone

4. Message is passed along a relay neurone

CNS

6. When message reaches muscle, it contracts to move arm away from bee

3. Message travels along the sensory neurone

2. Stimulation of the pain receptor

1. Cheeky bee stings finger

1) The neurones in reflex arcs go through the spinal cord or through an unconscious part of the brain.

2) When a stimulus (e.g. a painful bee sting) is detected by receptors, impulses are sent along a sensory neurone to the CNS.

3) In the CNS the sensory neurone passes on the message to a relay neurone.

4) Relay neurones relay the impulses to a motor neurone.

5) The impulses then travel along the motor neurone to the effector (a muscle in this example).

6) The muscle then contracts and moves your hand away from the bee.

7) Because you don't have to think about the response (which takes time), it's quicker than normal responses.

Here's a block diagram of a reflex arc — it shows what happens, from stimulus to response.

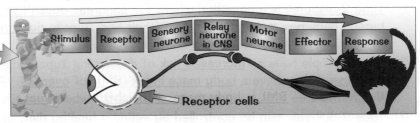

| Stimulus | Receptor | Sensory neurone | Relay neurone in CNS | Motor neurone | Effector | Response |

Receptor cells

Don't get all twitchy — just learn it...

Listen up... GCSE Science isn't just a test of what you know, it's also a test of how well you can apply knowledge. So don't worry if you're asked about a different reflex — the reflex arc is the same, so just apply what you know.

*Don't try this at home, it'll spoil your mum's ironing board.

Insulin and Diabetes

Blood glucose is controlled as part of <u>homeostasis</u> (see page 20), using the hormones <u>insulin</u> and <u>glucagon</u>.

Insulin <u>and</u> Glucagon Control Blood Sugar Level

1) Eating foods containing <u>carbohydrate</u> puts <u>glucose</u> (a type of sugar) into the blood from the gut.
2) The normal metabolism of cells <u>removes</u> glucose from the blood.
3) Vigorous <u>exercise</u> removes much more glucose from the blood.
4) To control the <u>level</u> of blood glucose there has to be a way to <u>add or remove</u> glucose from the blood...

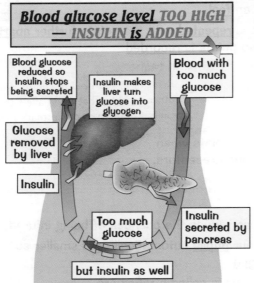

Blood glucose level *TOO HIGH* — **INSULIN** *is* ADDED

Blood glucose reduced so insulin stops being secreted

Insulin makes liver turn glucose into glycogen

Blood with too much glucose

Glucose removed by liver

Insulin

Too much glucose

Insulin secreted by pancreas

but insulin as well

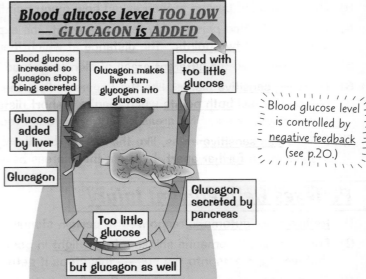

Blood glucose level *TOO LOW* — **GLUCAGON** *is* ADDED

Blood glucose increased so glucagon stops being secreted

Glucagon makes liver turn glycogen into glucose

Blood with too little glucose

Glucose added by liver

Glucagon

Too little glucose

Glucagon secreted by pancreas

but glucagon as well

Blood glucose level is controlled by <u>negative feedback</u> (see p.20.)

Type 1 Diabetes — Caused by a Lack of Insulin

1) <u>Type 1 diabetes</u> is a condition where the <u>pancreas produces little or no insulin</u>. The result is that a person's blood sugar can <u>rise</u> to a level that can <u>kill them</u>.

2) The problem needs to be <u>controlled</u> in the following ways:
   a) <u>Limiting the intake of foods</u> rich in simple carbohydrates, i.e. sugars (which cause the blood glucose level to rise rapidly).
   b) <u>Insulin therapy</u> — this usually involves <u>injecting insulin</u> into the blood several times a day. It's often done at <u>mealtimes</u> so that the liver <u>removes</u> the <u>glucose</u> quickly once the food has been <u>digested</u>. This stops the level of glucose in the blood from getting too high and is a <u>very effective treatment</u>.

3) Insulin is usually injected into <u>subcutaneous tissue</u> (fatty tissue just under the skin).

4) The <u>amount of insulin</u> that needs to be injected depends on the person's <u>diet</u> and how <u>active</u> they are, e.g.
   • Eating a <u>healthy diet reduces</u> the amount of insulin that needs to be injected.
   • Doing <u>regular exercise</u> also <u>reduces</u> the amount of insulin that needs to be injected.

Remember, insulin <u>reduces</u> blood sugar level.

Type 2 Diabetes — a Person is Resistant to Insulin

1) <u>Type 2 diabetes</u> is a condition where the <u>pancreas doesn't produce enough insulin</u> or when a person becomes <u>resistant to insulin</u> (their body's cells <u>don't respond</u> properly to the hormone). In both of these cases, blood sugar level <u>rises</u>.

2) Obese people have an <u>increased risk</u> of developing Type 2 diabetes. People are classified as <u>obese</u> if they have a <u>body mass index</u> (<u>BMI</u>) of <u>over 30</u>. BMI is worked out using this formula — <u>BMI = body mass ÷ (height)^2</u>, where <u>mass</u> is in <u>kg</u> and <u>height</u> is in <u>m</u>.

3) Type 2 diabetes can be <u>controlled</u> by eating a <u>healthy diet</u>, getting regular <u>exercise</u> and <u>losing weight</u> if needed. Some people with Type 2 diabetes also have <u>medication</u> or <u>insulin injections</u>.

And people used to think the pancreas was just a cushion... *(true)*

So <u>Type 2 diabetes</u> is linked to <u>obesity</u>, but scientists are still researching exactly <u>how</u> they're linked.

Plant Growth Hormones

Plants have hormones too, you know. Not that you'll ever see one scoffing a chocolate bar on a bad day.

Plants Respond to Different Stimuli

1) Plants can respond to stimuli (e.g. light, gravity or moisture) by regulating their growth.
2) A plant's growth response is called a tropism. A positive tropism is growing towards a stimulus.
3) You need to know these two responses:

PHOTOTROPISM — the growth of a plant in response to light. Shoots are positively phototropic — they grow towards light.

GRAVITROPISM (GEOTROPISM) — the growth of a plant in response to gravity. Roots are positively gravitropic — they grow downwards.

4) Plant growth hormones, e.g. auxin and gibberellin, allow plants to grow in response to stimuli.

Auxin Stimulates Plant Tips to Grow

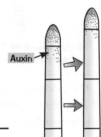

1) Auxin is a plant hormone that controls growth at the tips of shoots and roots.
2) Auxin is produced in the tips and diffuses backwards to stimulate the cells just behind the tips to elongate (grow longer).
3) If the tip of a shoot is removed, no auxin will be available and the shoot stops growing.
4) Auxin promotes growth in the shoot but high concentrations inhibit growth in the root — producing the desired result...

SHOOTS ARE POSITIVELY PHOTOTROPIC

1) When a shoot tip is exposed to light, more auxin accumulates on the side that's in the shade than the side that's in the light.
2) This makes the cells grow (elongate) faster on the shaded side, so the shoot bends towards the light.
3) This response enables plants to absorb more light for photosynthesis. Photosynthesis provides sugar, which provides energy for growth.

ROOTS ARE POSITIVELY GRAVITROPIC (GEOTROPIC)

1) When a root is growing sideways, gravity produces an unequal distribution of auxin in the tip, with more auxin on the lower side.
2) But in a root the extra auxin inhibits growth. This means the cells on top elongate faster, and the root bends downwards.
3) This response enables plants to extend their roots deep into the soil, so that they're well anchored. The plants can absorb more water and minerals, which are needed for photosynthesis.

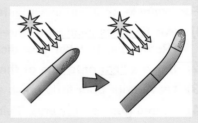

Gibberellin Stimulates Plant Stems to Grow

1) Gibberellin is another type of plant growth hormone.
2) It stimulates seed germination, stem growth and flowering.
3) It stimulates the stems of plants to grow by stem elongation — this helps plants to grow tall. If a dwarf variety of a plant is treated with gibberellin, it can grow to the same height as the tall variety.
4) Auxin and gibberellin can work together to have a really big effect on plant growth, e.g. together they help plants grow very tall.

What did the tall plant say to the short plant — you're talking gibberellish...

Who knew plants could be so hormonal... Not me for sure. The idea of plants having hormones might sound a trifle odd, but they make sure that plants grow in a useful direction, e.g. shoots grow towards light. Mmm, trifle.

Plant Growth Hormones — Experiments

You shouldn't just believe everything you read in Biology books, you know. They could tell you anything. But luckily for you, I always tell the truth — and here's some good old <u>classic plant experiments</u> to prove it.

You Need to be Able to <u>Interpret Experimental Data</u> on <u>Plant Hormones</u>

Take a look at these <u>two experiments</u>...

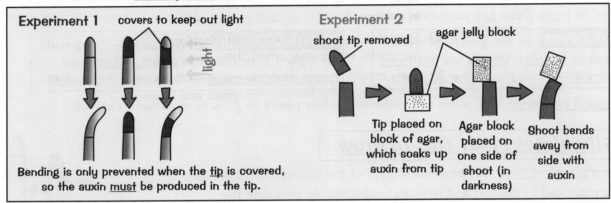

Experiment 1 — covers to keep out light

Bending is only prevented when the <u>tip</u> is covered, so the auxin <u>must</u> be produced in the tip.

Experiment 2 — shoot tip removed — agar jelly block

Tip placed on block of agar, which soaks up auxin from tip

Agar block placed on one side of shoot (in darkness)

Shoot bends away from side with auxin

...they show that auxin is <u>produced</u> in the <u>tip</u> of the plant (experiment 1) and causes <u>faster growth</u> on the side of the shoot where its <u>concentration</u> is <u>highest</u> (experiment 2). You need to be able to <u>interpret data</u> from experiments just like these — so make sure you know all about <u>auxin</u> and <u>gibberellin</u> from the previous page.

You can do a <u>Practical</u> to <u>Investigate Plant Growth Responses</u>

For example, you can investigate the effect of <u>light</u> on the <u>growth</u> of cress seeds like this...

1) Put <u>10 cress seeds</u> into three different Petri dishes, each lined with <u>moist filter paper</u>. (Remember to label your dishes, e.g. A, B, C.)

2) Shine a <u>light</u> onto one of the dishes from <u>above</u> and two of the dishes from <u>different directions</u> (see below).

3) Leave your poor little cress seeds alone for <u>one week</u>, what have they ever done to you...

4) ...until you can <u>observe</u> their <u>responses</u> — and hey presto, you'll find the seedlings <u>grow towards the light</u>.

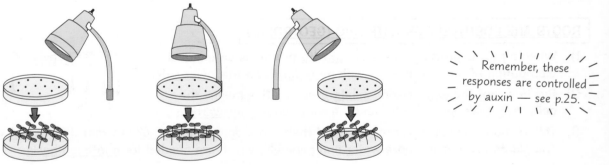

Remember, these responses are controlled by auxin — see p.25.

5) You know that the <u>growth response</u> of the cress seeds is due to <u>light</u> only, if you <u>control</u> all other variables.

Examples of variables that could <u>affect the experiment</u> and so need to be <u>controlled</u> are:

VARIABLE	HOW TO CONTROL IT
number of seeds	use the same number of seeds in each dish
type of seed	use seeds that all come from the same packet
temperature	use a thermometer to make sure the temperature of each dish is the same
water	use a measuring cylinder to add the same amount of water to each dish
light intensity	keep the distance between the bulb and dish the same for each dish

A plant auxin to a bar — 'ouch'...

...yeah I know, I know, but there's only so long I can cope with plant hormones before I go a bit doo-lally... So why not give yourself a break from my drivel — cover up the page, scribble down what you know, then see how much you got right. Anything you're not sure about, keep learning and learning till you know it.

Commercial Use of Plant Hormones

Plant hormones can be extracted, or artificial versions can be made. Then we can use them to do all kinds of useful things, including killing weeds, growing cuttings, ripening fruit and making seedless fruit.

1) As Selective Weedkillers

Unhappy weeds

1) Most weeds growing in fields of crops or in a lawn are broad-leaved, in contrast to grasses and cereals which have very narrow leaves.
2) Selective weedkillers have been developed from plant growth hormones which only affect the broad-leaved plants.
3) They totally disrupt their normal growth patterns, which soon kills them, whilst leaving the grass and crops untouched.

2) Growing from Cuttings with Rooting Powder

1) A cutting is part of a plant that has been cut off it, like the end of a branch with a few leaves on it.
2) Normally, if you stick cuttings in the soil they won't grow, but if you add rooting powder, which contains a plant growth hormone, they will produce roots rapidly and start growing as new plants.
3) This enables growers to produce lots of clones (exact copies) of a really good plant very quickly.

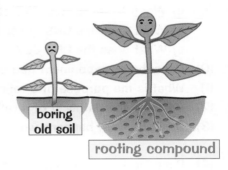
boring old soil
rooting compound

3) Controlling the Ripening of Fruit

1) The ripening of fruits can be controlled either while they are still on the plant, or during transport to the shops.
2) This allows the fruit to be picked while it's still unripe (and therefore firmer and less easily damaged).
3) Ripening hormone is then added and the fruit will ripen on the way to the supermarket and be perfect just as it reaches the shelves.

4) Producing Seedless Fruit

1) Fruit (with seeds in the middle) normally only grows on plants which have been pollinated by insects. If the plant doesn't get pollinated, the fruit and seeds don't grow.
2) If growth hormones are applied to the unpollinated flowers of some types of plant, the fruit will grow but the seeds won't. Some seedless citrus fruits can be grown this way.
3) Hormones are also used in the production of seedless grapes (although these are usually fertilised first).

Look, no pips...

You will ripen when I SAY you can ripen — and NOT BEFORE...

If you want some fruit to ripen, put them into a paper bag with a banana. The banana releases a ripening hormone called ethene which causes the fruit to ripen. Bad apples also release lots of ethene. Unfortunately, this means if you've got one bad apple in a barrel, you'll soon have lots of bad apples. See, every silver lining has a cloud.

Revision Summary for B1 Topic 2

This section covers everything you need to know about responding to change — homeostasis, nerves and hormones (including plant hormones). There's a lot to take in, so get yourself ready for some questions — they're the only way to find out if you really know your stuff. If the answers to these questions don't roll off your tongue immediately, I'm afraid you've got to go back to the page and relearn it. Here goes...

1)   What is homeostasis?
2)   Describe how body temperature is reduced when you're too hot.
3)   Describe how body temperature is increased when you're too cold.
4)   What are hormones?
5)   How do hormones travel around the body?
6)   What name is given to the chemicals found at synapses?
7)   List the four main differences between nerves and hormones.
8)   List the five sense organs and the receptors that each one contains.
9)   a) What do the letters CNS stand for?
     b) What does the CNS consist of?
     c) What does the CNS do?
10) Describe an experiment you could do to investigate the sensitivity of different areas of skin.
11) What is the purpose of a reflex?
12) Describe the pathway of a reflex arc from stimulus to response.
13) Describe what happens when blood glucose level is: a) too high
                                                          b) too low.
14) Describe the main ways in which Type 1 diabetes is controlled.
15) What does it mean if a person is 'resistant to insulin'?
16)* Sophie is 1.5 m tall and weighs 58 kg. a) What is her BMI?   b) Is she obese?
17) What is the name given to a plant's growth response to light?
18) What is auxin?
19) Shoots are positively phototropic. What does this mean?
20) Roots are positively gravitropic. Explain the role of auxin in this response.
21) List three things that gibberellin stimulates in plants.
22) Describe an experiment you could do to show phototropism in cress seedlings.
23) Explain how plant hormones are used as selective weedkillers.
24) Give three other ways that plant growth hormones are used commercially.

*Answer to this question is given on p.108

Drugs

Drugs alter what goes on in your body. Your body's essentially a seething mass of chemical reactions — drugs can interfere with these reactions, sometimes for the better, sometimes not.

Drugs Can be Beneficial or Harmful

1) Most drugs are chemical substances that affect the central nervous system.
   They cause changes in psychological behaviour and can be addictive (see below).

2) Some drugs are medically useful, such as antibiotics (e.g. penicillin).
   But many drugs are dangerous if misused.

3) This is why you can buy some drugs over the counter at a pharmacy, but others are restricted so you can only get them on prescription — your doctor decides if you should have them.

4) Some people get addicted to drugs — this means they have a physical need for the drug, and if they don't get it they get withdrawal symptoms. It's not just illegal drugs that are addictive — many legal ones are as well, e.g. caffeine in coffee. Caffeine withdrawal symptoms include irritability and shaky hands.

5) Tolerance develops with some drugs — the body gets used to having it and so you need a higher dose to give the same effect. This can happen with both legal drugs (e.g. alcohol), and illegal drugs (e.g. heroin).

6) If someone's addicted to a drug but wants to get off it, rehabilitation can help — this is where you get help and support to try and overcome an addiction.

You Need to Know All About These Drugs...

1) Depressants — e.g. alcohol. These decrease the activity of the brain. This slows down the responses of the nervous system, causing slow reactions (see below) and poor judgement of speed and distances (which is why drink driving is dangerous).

2) Stimulants — e.g. nicotine, caffeine. These do the opposite of depressants — they increase the activity of the brain, by increasing the amount of neurotransmitter at some neurone synapses (see page 21). This increases the speed of reactions, and makes you feel more alert and awake. Stimulant drugs are often used to treat depression.

3) Painkillers — e.g. narcotics like morphine. These decrease the feeling of pain. Different painkillers work in different ways. E.g. morphine is a strong painkiller that works by blocking the nerve impulses in the brain.

4) Hallucinogens — e.g. LSD. They distort what's seen and heard by altering the pathways nerve impulses normally travel along.

Reaction Time is How Quickly You Respond

Reaction time is the time it takes to respond to a stimulus (often less than a second). It can be affected by things like drugs. Reaction time can be measured like this...

1) One person holds a ruler vertically between the thumb and forefinger of a second person. They then let go without giving any warning.

2) The second person tries to catch the ruler as quickly as they can — as soon as they see it fall.

3) Reaction time is measured by how far down the ruler is caught — the further down, the slower their reactions.

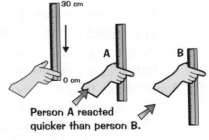

Person A reacted quicker than person B.

Person A beat person B at air hockey every time...

Make sure you learn the four different types of drug, and what they do, e.g. depressants slow down your reactions. Tiredness slows down reaction times too — so make sure you get a good night's sleep before your exam...

Smoking, Alcohol and Organ Transplants

Everyone knows that drinking and smoking don't do you much good. However, some people can damage their organs so much that the only option is an organ transplant.

Smoking Tobacco Can Cause Quite a Few Problems

1) Tobacco smoke contains carbon monoxide — this combines with haemoglobin in red blood cells, meaning the blood can carry less oxygen. In pregnant women, this can deprive the foetus of oxygen, leading to the baby being born underweight.

2) Tobacco smoke also contains carcinogens (chemicals that can lead to cancer), like tar. Lung cancer is way more common among smokers than non-smokers. It's estimated that 90% of lung cancers are associated with smoking (including passive smoking).

3) And to top it all off, smoking tobacco is addictive — because of the drug nicotine in tobacco smoke.

Alcohol Has Some Harmful Effects Too

Alcohol can affect a person straight away and in the future:

SHORT-TERM
1) Alcohol slows your reactions because it's a depressant (see page 29).
2) Being drunk leads to blurred vision and can also lower inhibitions — perhaps leading to people doing things they normally wouldn't.

LONG-TERM
1) Alcohol is poisonous. Normally, the liver breaks down the toxic alcohol into harmless by-products. But drinking too much too often causes the death of liver cells, forming scar tissue that starts to block blood flow through the liver — this is called cirrhosis. If the liver can't do its normal job of cleaning the blood, dangerous substances start to build up and damage the rest of the body.
2) Too much drinking can also lead to brain damage.

Organ Transplants Can Cure Diseases — But There Are Ethical Issues

If an organ's severely damaged (e.g. due to cirrhosis) it can be replaced by a donated natural organ.

1) Living donors can donate whole (or parts of) certain organs. For example, you can live with just one of your two kidneys and donate the other, or you can donate a piece of your liver.

2) Organs from people who have recently died, or who are brain dead, can also be transplanted.

3) But there's a big shortage of donors in the UK...

- You can join the NHS Organ Donor Register to show you're willing to donate organs after you die. However, doctors still need your family's consent before they can use the organs for a transplant.
- Some people say it should be made easier for doctors to use the organs of people who have died. One suggestion is to have an opt-out system instead — this means anyone's organs can be used unless the person has registered to say they don't want them to be donated.

4) Because of the organ shortage, some people may be less likely to get an organ transplant (e.g. if they are unlikely to survive the operation). Other people may only be considered if they change their lifestyle, e.g:
- Obese (very overweight) people can have a greater risk of dying after surgery, so they might have to lose weight before they are considered for organ transplants e.g. heart transplants.
- People who have damaged their liver through drinking too much alcohol might not be considered for liver transplants unless they stop drinking — more alcohol would damage their new liver.

5) Some people think that those who have harmed their own organs don't deserve an organ transplant as much as those people whose organs have been damaged through illness. But transplant guidelines aren't based on who would "deserve" a transplant, but who is most likely to benefit.

I think I need a brain transplant to learn all this lot...

In the exam you might have to evaluate data on smoking and its effects on health. So make sure you know the difference between correlation and cause (see page 7). A correlation doesn't always equal cause.

Infectious Diseases

An infectious disease is a disease that can be transmitted from one person to another (so obviously not all diseases are infectious). Sounds like it's going to be a cheery topic...

Infectious Diseases are Caused by Pathogens

1) Pathogens are microorganisms (microbes) that cause disease.
2) They include some bacteria, protozoa (certain single-celled creatures), fungi and all viruses.
3) Pathogens can spread in different ways:

Water	Some pathogens can be picked up by drinking or bathing in dirty water. E.g. Cholera is a bacterial infection that causes diarrhoea and dehydration. It's spread when drinking water is contaminated with the diarrhoea of other sufferers.
Food	Other pathogens are picked up by eating contaminated food. E.g. Salmonella bacteria cause food poisoning and are found in food that has been kept too long or not cooked properly.
Air	Airborne pathogens are carried in the air in droplets produced when you cough or sneeze — so other people can breathe them in. E.g. the influenza virus that causes flu is spread this way.
Contact	Some pathogens can be picked up by touching contaminated surfaces, including the skin. E.g. athlete's foot is a fungus which makes skin itch and flake off. It's most commonly spread by touching the same things as an infected person, e.g. shower floors and towels.
Body fluids	Some pathogens are spread by body fluids such as blood (e.g. by sharing needles to inject drugs), breast milk (through breast feeding) and semen (through sex). E.g. the HIV virus that causes AIDS (a disease which stops the immune system from working properly) is spread by body fluids.
Animal vectors	Vectors are animals that spread disease. Examples of vectors include: • Anopheles mosquito — it carries the protozoan that causes malaria (a disease that can damage the brain and kidneys or even be fatal). It spreads the disease by biting other organisms. • House fly — it carries the bacterium that causes dysentery (a disease that causes severe diarrhoea). It spreads the disease by carrying the bacteria onto food.

Physical and Chemical Barriers Stop Pathogens Entering the Body

You need to know about two different types of barrier against pathogens — physical and chemical.

PHYSICAL BARRIERS

1) The SKIN

Undamaged skin is a very effective barrier against microorganisms.

And if it gets damaged, blood clots quickly to seal cuts and keep microorganisms out.

2) The RESPIRATORY SYSTEM

The whole respiratory tract (nasal passage, trachea and lungs) is lined with mucus and cilia. The mucus catches dust and bacteria before they reach the lungs and the cilia push the gunk-filled mucus away from the lungs.

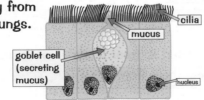

cilia

mucus

goblet cell (secreting mucus)

nucleus

CHEMICAL BARRIERS

1) The EYES

Eyes produce (in tears) a chemical called lysozyme which kills bacteria on the surface of the eye.

2) The STOMACH

If you eat food that contains pathogens, most of them will be killed by the hydrochloric acid in the stomach.

Coughs and sneezes spread diseases...

Lovely... anyway, after you've finished going eeuuurgh, make sure you remember the six different ways diseases can be spread and an example of a disease for each. Learn the four barriers too. And then wash your hands.

More About Drugs

I bet you've never <u>sat down</u> and had a <u>good think</u> about just how useful plants are to us.
They produce all sorts of <u>chemicals</u> which are dead useful...

Plants Can Produce Chemicals to Defend Themselves

1) When <u>plants</u> are attacked by pathogens they can produce <u>chemicals</u> to defend themselves.

2) Some of these chemicals have <u>antibacterial</u> effects that protect the plant against <u>bacteria</u>.

3) Humans have been using these <u>plant chemicals</u> for centuries.

> **EXAMPLE: TEA TREE**
> - The <u>tea tree</u> is a large Australian shrub — its leaves produce an <u>oil</u> that <u>kills bacteria</u>.
> - The indigenous people of Australia have used these leaves in their <u>traditional medicines</u> for centuries.
> - These days the <u>purified oil</u> is used in all sorts of <u>antibacterial products</u>, e.g. <u>facial cleansers</u>.

Antiseptics Are Used Outside The Body To Stop Disease Spreading

1) <u>Antiseptics</u> are chemicals that <u>destroy bacteria</u> or <u>stop them growing</u>.

2) Antiseptics are used <u>outside</u> the body to help to <u>clean wounds</u> and <u>surfaces</u>. They're used to <u>prevent infection</u> rather than treat it.

3) Plenty of <u>household products</u> contain antiseptics, e.g. bathroom cleaners.

4) Antiseptics are used in <u>hospitals</u> and surgeries to try to prevent the spread of infections like MRSA (p.33).

Antibiotics Are Used Inside The Body To Treat Infections

1) Antibiotics are drugs used <u>inside</u> the body, usually taken as a pill or injected.

2) They are used to treat patients who are <u>already infected</u> with <u>bacteria</u> or <u>fungi</u>.

3) However, antibiotics don't destroy <u>viruses</u> (e.g. flu and cold viruses).

4) There are two types of <u>antibiotics</u>:

ANTIBACTERIALS
1) <u>Antibacterial antibiotics</u> (e.g. penicillin) are used to treat bacterial infections.
2) They work by <u>killing</u> bacteria or stopping them from <u>growing</u>.
3) However, bacteria can evolve <u>resistance</u> to certain antibacterial antibiotics — meaning the antibiotics <u>don't work any more</u> (see page 33).

ANTIFUNGALS
1) <u>Antifungal antibiotics</u> (e.g. nystatin) are used to treat fungal infections.
2) They work by <u>killing</u> the fungi or stopping them from <u>growing</u>.

Imagine the hilarity when my Dad's sister married Mr. Biotic...

So, we can take the <u>chemicals</u> that plants make to stop them being infected by <u>pathogens</u>, turn them into <u>useful products</u> and use them for our own benefits... How amazingly good is that? Even if you don't think so, just make sure you learn the page anyway, including the <u>differences</u> between <u>antiseptics</u>, <u>antibacterials</u> and <u>antifungals</u>.

Antiseptics and Antibiotics

The discovery of the first antibiotic was a huge one — suddenly infections that had been fatal could be cured.

Bacteria Can Become Resistant to Antibiotics

1) Bacteria can mutate — sometimes the mutations cause them to be resistant to (not killed by) an antibiotic.

2) If you have an infection, some of the bacteria might be resistant to antibiotics.

3) This means that when you treat the infection, only the non-resistant strains of bacteria will be killed.

4) The individual resistant bacteria will survive and reproduce, and the population of the resistant strain will increase. This is an example of natural selection (see page 15).

5) This resistant strain could cause a serious infection that can't be treated by antibiotics. E.g. MRSA (methicillin-resistant *Staphylococcus aureus*) causes serious wound infections and is resistant to the powerful antibiotic methicillin.

6) Misuse of antibiotics (e.g. doctors overprescribing them or patients not finishing a course) has increased the rate of development of resistant strains. So nowadays you won't get antibiotics for a mild infection, only for something more serious.

You Can do a Practical to Investigate Antibiotics and Antiseptics

You can test the action of antibiotics by growing cultures of microorganisms:

1) Pour hot, sterilised agar jelly into a sterile Petri dish (a shallow round plastic dish). (The jelly is a culture medium that contains the carbohydrates, minerals, proteins and vitamins that microorganisms need to grow.)

2) When the jelly's cooled and set, transfer bacteria to the culture medium.

3) Then take three paper discs — soak one disc in an antibiotic (disc A), another in a different antibiotic (disc B) and the third in sterile water (disc C).

4) Place the discs onto the jelly (labelling the bottom of the dish to show which disc is which) and tape the lid onto the dish.

5) Leave the dish for 24 hours at 25 °C. (The bacteria will multiply and grow into a 'lawn' covering the jelly.)

6) After that time look at the Petri dish for the results:

- Anywhere the bacteria can't grow is called an "inhibition zone". The bigger the inhibition zone around a disc, the more effective the antibiotic is. E.g. in the diagram, antibiotic A is more effective than antibiotic B because it has a bigger inhibition zone.

- There will be no inhibition zone around disc C because it's a control — it shows that it is the antibiotic and not the paper disc that is stopping the bacteria from growing.

No inhibition zone around an antibiotic disc could mean that the bacteria are resistant to it (see top of page).

7) The control variables for this experiment include:
- Temperature (e.g. don't leave one side of the dish near a radiator).
- Size of the discs.
- Concentration of the antibiotics.

8) Remember you can carry out exactly the same experiment as above using different antiseptics.

Agar — my favourite jelly flavour after raspberry...

Microorganisms might be the perfect pets. You don't have to walk them, they won't get lonely and they hardly cost anything to feed. But whatever you do, do not feed them after midnight.

Energy and Biomass

All living things are interdependent — organisms depend on each other for things like food, pollination, shelter, etc. in order to survive and reproduce. A simple example is that bees depend on flowers for nectar (food), and flowers depend on bees for pollination.

Some Energy Passes Along The Food Chain — But Most Is Lost

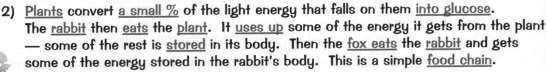

1) Energy from the Sun is the source of energy for nearly all life on Earth.

2) Plants convert a small % of the light energy that falls on them into glucose. The rabbit then eats the plant. It uses up some of the energy it gets from the plant — some of the rest is stored in its body. Then the fox eats the rabbit and gets some of the energy stored in the rabbit's body. This is a simple food chain.

3) Energy is used up at each stage to stay alive, i.e. in respiration, which powers all life processes, including movement. A lot of energy is lost to the surroundings as heat. This is especially true for mammals and birds, whose bodies must be kept at a constant temperature — normally higher than their surroundings.

4) This energy is said to be 'lost' — it doesn't actually disappear but the next animal in the food chain can't use it.

5) Material and energy are also lost from the food chain in droppings — if you set dried droppings alight they burn, proving they still have chemical energy in them.

6) This explains why you hardly ever get food chains with more than about five trophic levels. So much energy is lost at each stage that there's not enough left to support more organisms after four or five stages.

Pyramids of Biomass Show Weight

1) Biomass is how much the creatures at each level of a food chain would weigh if you put them together.

2) This biomass is a store of energy (see above). So a pyramid of biomass also shows how much energy there is at each stage in the food chain.

3) The pyramid of biomass below shows the food chain of a mini meadow ecosystem. The dandelions are the producer (starting point) — they're eaten by the rabbits (primary consumers), which are eaten by the fox (secondary consumer)... and so on.

4) If you weighed them, all the dandelions would have a big biomass and the hundreds of fleas would have a very small biomass. Biomass pyramids are always a pyramid shape.

Fleas	2 g	(not even slightly
Fox	4 kg	to scale...)
Rabbits	40 kg	
Dandelions	1000 kg	

5) Each time you go up one level (one trophic level if you fancy showing off), the mass of organisms goes down. This is because most of the biomass (or energy) is lost (as shown above) and so does not become biomass in the next level up.

Don't forget that if you get a question on biomass in the exam you need to include the units. And if you're asked to draw a pyramid, make sure it's to scale.

Pyramids of Biomass — the eighth wonder of the world...

Pyramids of biomass are a way of describing food chains quantitatively (rather than just saying 'foxes eat rabbits', you say what mass of foxes eats what mass of rabbits, etc.). Don't forget that there's energy in that biomass and that energy is lost each time you go up a level in the pyramid e.g. in droppings, through movement.

Parasitism and Mutualism

For some species, their survival is almost completely <u>dependent</u> on another species. In a <u>parasitic</u> relationship, only <u>one</u> benefits — the other often suffers. But in a <u>mutualistic</u> relationship, <u>both</u> species benefit.

Parasites _Take Without Giving_ Anything In Return

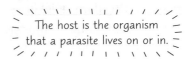

PARASITES live in or on a host. They <u>take</u> what they need to survive, <u>without</u> giving anything <u>back</u>. This often <u>harms</u> the host — which makes it a win-lose situation. Here are some examples:

> The host is the organism that a parasite lives on or in.

FLEAS
<u>Fleas</u> are insects that live in the fur and bedding of animals, including <u>humans</u>. They <u>feed</u> by <u>sucking the blood</u> of their hosts and can reproduce quickly. Their hosts <u>gain nothing</u> from having fleas (unless you count hundreds of bites).

HEAD LICE
<u>Head lice</u> are insects that live on <u>human scalps</u>, sucking <u>blood</u> for <u>food</u> and making the person <u>itch</u>.

TAPEWORMS
<u>Tapeworms</u> attach to the <u>intestinal wall</u> of their hosts (e.g. humans). They absorb lots of <u>nutrients</u> from the host, causing them to suffer from <u>malnutrition</u>.

MISTLETOE
<u>Mistletoe</u> is a <u>parasitic plant</u> that grows on <u>trees and shrubs</u>. It absorbs <u>water</u> and <u>nutrients</u> from its host, which can <u>reduce</u> the <u>host's growth</u>.

Both _Organisms Gain_ From a _Mutualistic_ Relationship

MUTUALISM is a relationship where <u>both</u> organisms benefit — so it's a win-win relationship. For example:

OXPECKERS
<u>Oxpeckers</u> are birds that live on the backs of <u>buffalo</u>. Not only do they <u>eat pests</u> on the buffalo, like ticks, flies and maggots (providing the oxpeckers with a source of <u>food</u>), but they also <u>alert</u> the animal to any <u>predators</u> that are near, by hissing. Oxpeckers are an example of a <u>cleaner species</u>.

CLEANER FISH
Another example of cleaner species are <u>cleaner fish</u> (e.g. <u>cleaner wrasses</u>) that eat <u>dead skin</u> and <u>parasites</u> off <u>larger fish</u> (e.g. <u>groupers</u>). In return they get a source of <u>food</u>, and avoid being <u>eaten</u> by the big fish.

NITROGEN-FIXING BACTERIA IN LEGUMES
Most plants have to rely on <u>nitrogen-fixing bacteria</u> in the soil to get the <u>nitrates</u> that they need. But <u>leguminous plants</u> (beans, peas, clover etc.) carry the bacteria in <u>nodules</u> in their <u>roots</u>. The bacteria get a constant supply of <u>sugar</u> from the plant, and the plant gets essential <u>nitrates</u> from the bacteria.

CHEMOSYNTHETIC BACTERIA IN DEEP-SEA VENTS
Some <u>chemosynthetic bacteria</u> live inside <u>giant tube worms</u> or in the gills of <u>molluscs</u> in <u>deep-sea vents</u> (see page 14). The tube worms supply the bacteria with <u>chemicals</u> from the seawater, which the bacteria turn into <u>food</u> for themselves <u>and</u> the host worms.

Revision stress — don't let it eat you up...

Ugh... I can't believe there are animals out there that actually eat ticks and maggots. Makes me feel ill just thinking about it. That said, I do like the idea of something watching my back — that's kinda cool.

Human Activity and the Environment

Whichever way you look at it, human activity has an <u>enormous impact</u> on the environment...

A Larger Population Affects the Environment More

1) The <u>population</u> of the world is currently <u>rising pretty darn quickly</u> — as the graph shows.
2) This is mostly due to <u>modern medicine</u>, which has stopped widespread death from <u>disease</u>.
3) It's also due to modern farming methods, which can now provide the <u>food</u> needed for so many hungry mouths.
4) The effect of this is quite simple: MORE HUMANS = GREATER IMPACT.
5) There are potential problems...
   i) raw materials, including <u>non-renewable</u> energy resources, are rapidly being <u>used up</u>,
   ii) more and more <u>waste</u> is being <u>produced</u>,
   iii) more and more <u>pollutants</u> are being <u>produced</u>, including <u>phosphates</u> (e.g. from detergents), <u>nitrates</u> (e.g. from fertilisers) and <u>sulfur dioxide</u> (e.g. from coal-burning power stations).

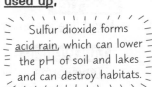

Sulfur dioxide forms <u>acid rain</u>, which can lower the pH of soil and lakes and can destroy habitats.

Fertilisers Help Crops But Harm Water Life

1) <u>Fertilisers</u> which contain <u>nitrates</u> are essential to <u>modern farming</u>. Without them crops wouldn't grow nearly so well, and <u>food yields</u> would be <u>well down</u>. This is because the crops take <u>nitrates</u> out of the soil and these nitrates need to be <u>replaced</u>.
2) The <u>problems</u> start if some of the <u>rich fertiliser</u> finds its way into <u>rivers</u>, <u>lakes</u> and <u>seas</u>.
3) This happens quite easily if <u>too much fertiliser</u> is applied, especially if it rains soon afterwards.
4) The result is <u>eutrophication</u> — <u>too many nitrates</u> in the water cause a sequence of "<u>mega-growth</u>, <u>mega-death</u> and <u>mega-decay</u>" involving most of the <u>plant</u> and <u>animal life</u> in the water.

| Excess nitrate washes into river causing rapid growth of algae. | → | Some plants start dying due to competition for light. | → | Microbe numbers increase as they feed on the dead material. | → | Microbes use up all the oxygen. Fish and other aquatic animals suffocate. |

Raw sewage pumped into rivers also causes eutrophication.

You Can Do a Practical To Show the Effect of Pollutants on Plant Growth

1) Set up one jam jar with <u>moist cotton wool</u>, soaked in water, and <u>20 cress seeds</u> on top — this is the control.
2) Set up a second jar in the <u>same way</u>, but with the cotton wool soaked in a solution of <u>pollutant</u>, e.g. <u>nitrate</u>.
3) <u>Seal</u> each jar with its <u>lid</u>.
4) After <u>5-7 days</u>, <u>measure</u> the <u>length</u> of the <u>shoots</u> and work out the <u>average shoot length</u> for each jar.
5) The results will depend on the pollutant used. E.g. <u>nitrate</u> will cause <u>increased</u> plant growth compared to the control.
6) Make sure the following <u>variables</u> are <u>controlled</u> — <u>temperature</u>, <u>amount of light</u>, <u>volume of solution</u> that cotton wool absorbs, <u>number of seeds</u> and <u>type of seed</u> for each dish, so you know the effect on plant growth is <u>only due</u> to the pollutant.
7) This experiment can also be used to show the effect of <u>pollutants</u> on plant <u>germination</u> (when a seed starts to grow into a plant).

SIDE VIEW — BEFORE · SIDE VIEW — AFTER 5-7 DAYS · shoot · length of shoot · seed · jam jar · moist cotton wool

Essential to plants, and essential to your biology revision...

<u>Nitrates</u> are essential to <u>plant growth</u> — so farmers add fertilisers to increase their crop yields. They could make your cress grow rampantly. But other pollutants like sulphur dioxide harm plants — expect fewer, smaller plants.

Recycling

Recycling is a good thing that humans can do to reduce our impact on the environment.
It means reusing resources, rather than using them once and chucking them in a waste dump.

Recycling Conserves Our Natural Resources

If materials aren't recycled they get thrown away as waste. This means that:

1) There is more waste, so more land has to be used for landfill sites (waste dumps).
Some waste is toxic (poisonous), so this also means more polluted land.

2) More materials have to be manufactured or extracted to make new products (rather than recycling existing ones) — using up more of the Earth's resources and more energy.

Recycling uses up less of the Earth's natural resources. Recycling processes usually use less energy and create less pollution than manufacturing or extracting materials from scratch. Recyclable materials include:

1) **Metals** Metals are extracted from ores (e.g. aluminium is extracted from bauxite).
There's a limited amount of metal ore — by recycling we make the most of what we've got.
Mining and extracting metals takes lots of energy, most of which comes from burning fossil fuels.
So recycling metals uses less of our limited resources of fossil fuels and means less CO_2 is released.

2) **Paper** Paper is produced from wood. Recycling paper means that fewer trees have to be cut down, which helps to prevent deforestation. Recycling paper uses 28%-70% less energy than manufacturing new paper.

3) **Plastics** Most plastics are made from crude oil — so recycling plastics helps to conserve our oil resources. Plastics are really slow to decompose — if they're thrown away (rather than recycled), they take up space in landfill sites for years.

There are Some Problems with Recycling

1) Recycling still uses energy, e.g. for collecting, sorting, cleaning and processing waste.

2) Some waste materials can be difficult and time-consuming to sort out, e.g. different types of plastic have to be separated from each other before they can be recycled.

3) The equipment needed for recycling can be expensive, e.g. equipment for sorting plastics automatically.

4) In some cases, the quality of recycled materials isn't as good as new materials, e.g. recycled paper.

5) Some materials can only be recycled a limited number of times (e.g. plastics, paper). Others can be recycled indefinitely though (e.g. aluminium).

The UK Produces a Lot of Waste — and Could Recycle More

1) England and Wales produce over 100 million tonnes of domestic, commercial and industrial waste a year.

2) The amount of waste recycled in the UK is increasing — but it's still not as much as some other European countries.

3) New laws are being introduced in the UK and the European Union (EU) to increase recycling, e.g. by 2015, EU law requires that cars will have to be made of 95% recyclable materials.

Recycling — doing the Tour de France twice...

Recycling isn't perfect — but it's generally a lot better than dumping all our rubbish in a big hole in the ground. Do your bit — reuse plastic bags and recycle your drinks cans.

Indicator Species

Some organisms <u>can't</u> live in areas where there is <u>polluted water</u> or <u>air</u>, but other organisms can. <u>Both</u> of these types of organism can be <u>monitored</u> and used as <u>indicators</u> of pollution — handy, as they're easy to spot, and show pollution levels over days and months.

Indicator Species <u>Are Used to Show The</u> Level <u>of...</u>

Some <u>organisms</u> are very <u>sensitive to changes</u> in their environment and so can be studied to see the effect of human activities — these organisms are known as <u>indicator species</u>.

① Water Pollution

1) If <u>raw sewage</u> or other pollutants containing <u>nitrates</u> are released into a <u>river</u>, the <u>bacterial population</u> in the water increases and uses up the <u>oxygen</u> (see page 36).

2) Some invertebrate animals, like <u>stonefly larvae</u> and <u>freshwater shrimps</u> are <u>good indicators</u> for water pollution because they're <u>very sensitive</u> to the concentration of <u>dissolved oxygen</u> in the water. If you find stonefly larvae in a river, it <u>indicates</u> that the <u>water is clean</u>.

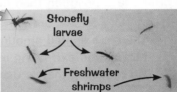
Stonefly larvae
Freshwater shrimps

3) Other <u>invertebrate</u> species have adapted to live in <u>polluted conditions</u> — so if you see a lot of them you know there's a problem. E.g. <u>blood worms</u> and <u>sludgeworms</u> indicate a <u>very high level of water pollution</u>.

② Air Pollution

1) <u>Air pollution</u> can be monitored by looking at particular types of <u>lichen</u> that are very sensitive to the concentration of <u>sulfur dioxide</u> in the atmosphere (and so can give a good idea about the level of pollution from <u>car exhausts</u>, power stations, etc.). The number and type of lichen at a particular location will indicate <u>how clean</u> the air is (e.g. the air is <u>clean</u> if there are <u>lots of lichen</u>).

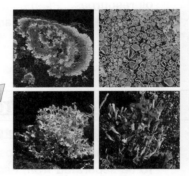

2) <u>Blackspot fungus</u> is found on <u>rose leaves</u>. It is also sensitive to the level of sulfur dioxide in the air, so its presence will indicate <u>clean air</u>.

3) You might get some data on indicator species in the exam, e.g. data showing there are <u>more</u> lichen species <u>further away</u> from a city centre. This is probably because outside the city centre, there is <u>less pollution</u> and the air contains <u>less sulfur dioxide</u> and other pollutants.

<u>Non-living Indicators</u> <u>Can Also Show The</u> Level of Pollution

1) <u>Dissolved oxygen meters</u> and <u>chemical tests</u> are used to measure the concentration of dissolved oxygen in water, to show how the level of <u>water pollution</u> is changing.

2) <u>Electronic meters</u> and various <u>laboratory tests</u> are also used to measure the concentration of <u>sulfur dioxide</u> in air, to show how <u>air pollution</u> is changing.

Teenagers are an indicator species — not found in clean rooms...

Don't forget that the <u>absence</u> of an indicator species could mean the <u>opposite</u> of what they indicate. E.g. the <u>absence</u> of <u>stonefly larvae</u> could indicate <u>polluted water</u>. Nice and simple, innit?

The Carbon Cycle

Carbon flows through the Earth's ecosystems in the <u>carbon cycle</u>. The beauty of the carbon cycle is that carbon is <u>recycled</u> — it's <u>used by organisms</u> but then ends up back in the atmosphere again.

The <u>Carbon Cycle</u> **Shows How** <u>Carbon</u> **is** <u>Recycled</u>

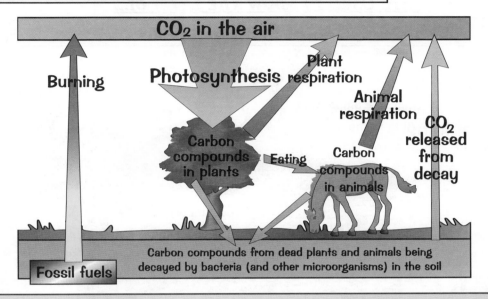

This diagram isn't half as bad as it looks. <u>Learn</u> these important points:

1) There's only <u>one arrow</u> going <u>down</u>. The only thing that <u>removes CO$_2$</u> from the atmosphere is <u>photosynthesis</u> — plants use it to make carbohydrates, fats and proteins.

2) <u>Eating</u> passes the carbon compounds in the plant along to <u>animals</u> in a food chain or web.

3) Both plant and animal <u>respiration</u> put CO$_2$ <u>back into the atmosphere</u>.

4) Plants and animals eventually <u>die</u> and <u>decay</u>.

5) When plants and animals <u>decay</u> they're broken down by <u>bacteria</u> and <u>fungi</u>.
These decomposers <u>release CO$_2$</u> back into the air by <u>respiration</u> as they break down the material.

6) <u>Fossil fuels</u> (made of decayed plant and animal matter) are <u>burned</u> (<u>combustion</u>).
This also <u>releases CO$_2$</u> back into the air.

<u>Nutrients</u> **are Constantly** <u>Recycled</u>

1) <u>Living things</u> are made of elements they take from the world around them.

2) It's not just carbon that plants take from the environment. <u>Plants</u> also take elements like <u>oxygen</u>, <u>hydrogen</u> and <u>nitrogen</u> (see the next page) from the <u>soil</u> or the <u>air</u>. They turn these elements into the <u>complex compounds</u> (carbohydrates, proteins and fats) that make up living organisms.

3) These elements are <u>returned</u> to the environment in <u>waste products</u> produced by the organisms, or when the organisms <u>die</u>. Dead organisms decay because they're <u>broken down</u> by <u>decomposers</u> — that's how the elements get put back into the <u>soil</u>.

4) All the important <u>elements</u> are <u>recycled</u> — they return to the soil or air, ready to be <u>used</u> by new <u>plants</u> and put back into the <u>food chain</u>.

What goes around, comes around...

In many ecosystems (like forests and prairies) the materials <u>taken out</u> of the soil and air are <u>balanced</u> by those that are put <u>back in</u>. There's a constant <u>cycle</u> happening. Changing ecosystems (e.g. bogs accumulating peat, plantations where trees are removed) don't exactly balance though. The <u>cycle</u> still happens, it's just a bit <u>wonky</u>.

The Nitrogen Cycle

The flow of nitrates through the atmosphere, soil and living organisms is called the nitrogen cycle. It's similar to the carbon cycle (last page) — but a tad more complicated...

The Nitrogen Cycle is the Flow of Nitrogen Through Nature

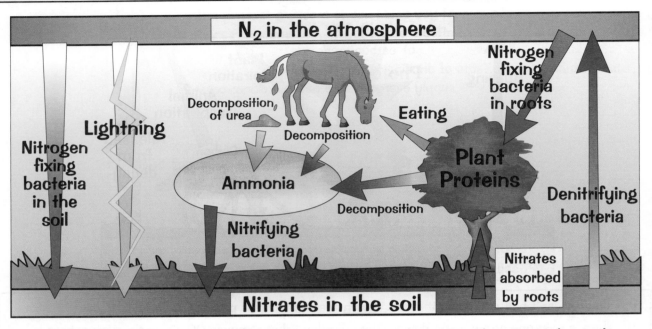

1) The atmosphere contains 78% nitrogen gas, N_2. This is very unreactive and so it can't be used directly by plants or animals.

2) Nitrogen is needed for making proteins for growth, so living organisms have to get it somehow.

3) Nitrogen in the air has to be turned into nitrogen compounds, e.g. nitrates, before plants can use it. Plants absorb nitrates from the soil and use them to make proteins. Animals can only get proteins by eating plants (or each other) — so nitrogen compounds are passed along a food chain.

4) Decomposers (e.g. bacteria, fungi, worms) in the soil break down dead plants and animals. Decomposer bacteria turn proteins (from dead plants and animals) and urea (in animal waste) into ammonia.

5) Other soil bacteria called nitrifying bacteria convert this ammonia into nitrates. Since nitrates can be taken up by plants, the nitrogen in these organisms is recycled.

6) Nitrogen fixation isn't an obsession with nitrogen — it's the process of turning N_2 from the air into nitrogen compounds in the soil which plants can use. There are two main ways that this happens:
    a) Lightning — there's so much energy in a bolt of lightning that it's enough to make nitrogen react with oxygen in the air to give nitrates.
    b) Nitrogen-fixing bacteria in roots and soil (see below).

7) There are four different types of bacteria involved in the nitrogen cycle:

    a) DECOMPOSER BACTERIA — decompose proteins and urea and turn them into ammonia.
    b) NITRIFYING BACTERIA — turn ammonia in decaying matter into nitrates.
    c) NITROGEN-FIXING BACTERIA — turn atmospheric N_2 into nitrogen compounds that plants can use.
    d) DENITRIFYING BACTERIA — turn nitrates back into N_2 gas. This is of no benefit to living organisms.

8) Some nitrogen-fixing bacteria live in the soil. Others live in nodules on the roots of legume plants (e.g. peas and beans). This is why legume plants are so good at putting nitrogen back into the soil. The plants have a mutualistic relationship with the bacteria (see page 35).

I wish I had some information-fixing bacteria...

The nitrogen cycle is probably the scariest looking diagram you'll see in the whole of GCSE Science. But learn it you must. The horse being in the sky is just a bit of artistic licence...

Revision Summary for B1 Topic 3

It's that time again — time to see whether any of the stuff you've been reading has managed to soak through the fluff, mothballs and mouldy pizza boxes into your spongy old brain. Here we go...

1) How does a stimulant drug work? Give two examples of stimulants.
2) Briefly describe an experiment you could use to measure reaction times.
3) Briefly describe the harmful effects of the following chemicals found in cigarette smoke:
    a) nicotine   b) tar   c) carbon monoxide
4) State two long-term effects of drinking too much alcohol.
5) Are there enough organs to supply everyone who needs a donor organ?
6) What is a pathogen?
7) What is a vector?
8) State four different ways that pathogens can be spread, and give an example of each.
9) Name one chemical and one physical barrier that form part of the defence against pathogens.
10) What do plants produce to defend themselves from bacteria?
11) What are antiseptics?
12) Name the two types of antibiotics.
13) Name one type of bacteria that has developed resistance to certain antibiotics.
14) Why shouldn't your doctor give you antibiotics for a mild infection?
15) Where does the energy in a food chain originate? What happens to the energy?
16) Not all energy and biomass passes from one trophic level to the next. Where does the rest go?
17) Why are pyramids of biomass always pyramid shaped?
18) What is the difference between a parasitic and a mutualistic relationship?
19) Give an example of:
    a) a parasitic relationship   b) a mutualistic relationship
20) Give three ways in which an increasing human population has a greater effect on the environment.
21) Explain what eutrophication is.
22) Give two advantages and two disadvantages of recycling.
23) Give three types of material which can be recycled.
24) What does it mean if you find stonefly larvae in a river?
    a) There are no stones in the river.   b) The water is clean.   c) The water is dirty.
25) Explain how lichen can be used as an indicator of air pollution.
26) Sketch the carbon cycle.
27) Give two ways in which the elements an animal eats can be returned to the environment.
28) Why is nitrogen needed by plants and animals?
29) What do decomposers do?
30) Sketch out the nitrogen cycle.

The Evolution of the Atmosphere

For 200 million years or so, the atmosphere has been about how it is now: 78% nitrogen, 21% oxygen, and small amounts of other gases, mainly argon (nearly 1%) and a tiny amount of CO_2 (only 0.04%). There can be a lot of water vapour too. But it wasn't always like this. Here's how the past 4.5 billion years may have gone:

Phase 1 — *Volcanoes Gave Out Gases*

1) The Earth's surface was originally molten for many millions of years. It was so hot that any atmosphere just 'boiled away' into space.

2) Eventually things cooled down a bit and a thin crust formed, but volcanoes kept erupting.

3) The volcanoes gave out lots of gas — including carbon dioxide, water vapour and small amounts of other gases. We think this was how the oceans and atmosphere were formed.

4) According to this theory, the early atmosphere was probably mostly CO_2, with virtually no oxygen. This is quite like the atmospheres of Mars and Venus today.

5) The oceans formed when the water vapour condensed.

Holiday report: Not a nice place to be. Take strong walking boots and a good coat.

Phase 2 — *Green Plants Evolved and Produced Oxygen*

Holiday report: A bit slimy underfoot. Take wellies and a lot of suncream.

1) A lot of the early CO_2 dissolved into the oceans.

2) Later, marine organisms developed, which took in some of this CO_2. When they died the organisms were buried under layers of sediment and the CO_2 became 'locked up' in carbonate rocks.

3) Green plants evolved over most of the Earth. They were quite happy in the CO_2 atmosphere.

4) The green plants also removed CO_2 from the air and produced O_2 by photosynthesis. This caused the oxygen level to gradually increase.

Phase 3 — *Ozone Layer Allows Evolution of Complex Animals*

1) The build-up of oxygen in the atmosphere killed off some early organisms that couldn't tolerate it, but allowed other, more complex organisms to evolve and flourish.

2) The oxygen also created the ozone layer (O_3) which blocked harmful rays from the Sun and enabled even more complex organisms to evolve — us, eventually.

3) There is very little CO_2 left now.

Holiday report: A nice place to be. Visit before the crowds ruin it.

The atmosphere's evolving — shut the window will you...

It seems the atmosphere has been happily evolving away for 4.5 billion years or so — a lot longer than we've been around to watch it anyway. Break it up into three separate phases in your mind, and try to remember which gases go with each phase. Learn this and you'll soon evolve into a lovely young scientist.

Today's Atmosphere

Evidence for how the atmosphere evolved has been found in rocks and other sources. But no one was actually there, billions of years ago, to record the changes as they happened. So our theories about how today's atmosphere came about are just that — theories.

The Atmosphere is Still Changing

Human activity is changing the atmosphere:

1) <u>Burning fossil fuels</u> releases CO_2 — and as the world's become more industrialised, more fossil fuels have been burnt in power stations and in car engines.

2) <u>Deforestation</u> also contributes to the increase in CO_2 levels. Trees take in CO_2 from the atmosphere, so getting rid of a whole load of trees means more CO_2 is left in the atmosphere.

3) <u>Livestock farming</u> releases huge amounts of methane, CH_4, into the atmosphere — animals produce it when they pass wind (tee hee). The large population of dairy and beef cattle is to blame.

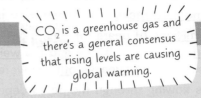
CO_2 is a greenhouse gas and there's a general consensus that rising levels are causing global warming.

Volcanic activity is changing the atmosphere:

1) <u>Sulfur dioxide</u> can be thrown high up into the atmosphere when volcanoes erupt. Sulfur dioxide gas reacts with sunlight, water, oxygen and dust to form volcanic smog.

2) <u>Carbon dioxide</u> is also released into the atmosphere by volcanic eruptions.

Sources of information on the evolution of the atmosphere are limited:

1) We've learned a lot about the past atmosphere from <u>Antarctic ice cores</u>. Each year, a layer of ice forms and <u>bubbles of air</u> get trapped inside it, then it's buried by the next layer. So the deeper the ice, the older the air — and if you examine the bubbles in different layers, you can see how the air has changed. The measurements have to be <u>ultra-precise</u> though, as the changes between layers can be very very tiny.

2) However, because no one was actually there at the time, it's difficult to be precise about exactly how the atmosphere has changed — some of it's down to guesswork.

You Can Investigate the Proportion of Oxygen in the Atmosphere

Here's a nice experiment that shows that the atmosphere today contains around <u>one fifth oxygen</u>.

1) When it's heated, <u>copper</u> reacts with oxygen in the air to make copper(II) oxide — so the reaction <u>uses up oxygen</u>.

2) If you heat an excess of copper in a tube and pass air over it using two <u>syringes</u>, you can use the markers on the syringes to tell <u>how much</u> oxygen has been used up.

You need to make sure that the system is sealed so no extra air can get in and out.

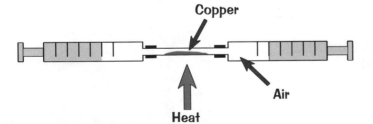

Copper

Air

Heat

The chemical equation for the reaction is:
$$2Cu + O_2 \rightarrow 2CuO$$

3) So, if you start with <u>100 cm³</u> of air, you'll end up with about <u>80 cm³</u> when the reaction's finished and the air has cooled. If <u>20 cm³</u> of air has gone then <u>around 20%</u> of the air must be oxygen.

CO_2 — the future of mobile technology...

Basically, we're the baddies in all this. We're driving around in big, fuel-greedy cars and farming more cows than you can shake a stick at. If we don't <u>stop</u> doing this we can expect a lot more changes in our atmosphere in the future... and all that careful evolving it's done will have been for nothing. Yikes.

The Three Different Types of Rock

Scientists classify rocks according to how they're formed. The three different types are: <u>sedimentary</u>, <u>metamorphic</u> and <u>igneous</u>. Sedimentary rocks are generally pretty soft, while igneous rocks are well hard.

There are *Three Steps* in the Formation of *Sedimentary Rock*

1) <u>Sedimentary rocks</u> are formed from <u>layers of sediment</u> laid down in <u>lakes</u> or <u>seas</u>.
2) Over <u>millions of years</u> the layers get <u>buried</u> under more layers and the <u>weight</u> pressing down <u>squeezes out</u> the water.
3) Fluids flowing through the pores deposit natural mineral <u>cement</u>.

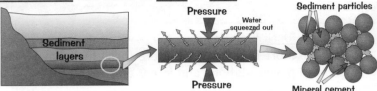

Limestone and Chalk are Sedimentary Rocks

1) Limestone and chalk are <u>sedimentary rocks</u> and they contain <u>fossils</u>. The rock isn't formed at high temperatures — so the remains and imprints of <u>dead organisms</u> aren't destroyed.
2) Limestone and chalk are easily <u>broken away</u> by wind, rain and waves — this is called <u>erosion</u> and it can change the shape of our landscape.

Metamorphic Rocks are Formed from Other Rocks

1) <u>Metamorphic rocks</u> are formed by the action of <u>heat and pressure</u> on <u>sedimentary</u> (or even <u>igneous</u>) <u>rocks</u> over <u>long periods</u> of time.
2) The <u>mineral structure</u> and <u>texture</u> may have changed, but the chemical composition is often the same as the original rock.
3) So long as the rocks don't actually <u>melt</u> they're classed as <u>metamorphic</u>. If they <u>melt</u> and turn to <u>magma</u>, they're <u>gone</u> (though they may eventually resurface as igneous rocks — see below).
4) <u>Marble</u> is formed from <u>limestone</u> or <u>chalk</u>. Very high temperatures <u>break down</u> the limestone and it reforms as <u>small crystals</u>. This gives marble a <u>more even texture</u> and makes it <u>much harder</u>.

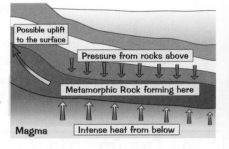

Igneous Rocks are Formed from Fresh Magma

1) <u>Igneous rocks</u> form when <u>molten magma</u> pushes up <u>into the crust</u> (or <u>right through it</u>) before cooling and solidifying. They contain various <u>different minerals</u> in <u>randomly arranged</u> interlocking <u>crystals</u>.
2) There are <u>two types</u> of igneous rocks, <u>extrusive</u> and <u>intrusive</u>:

> **EXTRUSIVE** igneous rocks cool **QUICKLY ABOVE GROUND**, forming **SMALL** crystals, e.g. basalt and rhyolite.

> **INTRUSIVE** igneous rocks cool **SLOWLY UNDERGROUND**, forming **BIG** crystals, e.g. granite and gabbro.

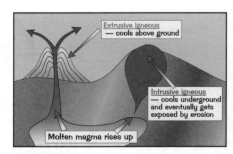

3) Granite is <u>very hard</u> (even harder than marble). It's ideal for <u>steps</u> and <u>buildings</u>.

Igneous rocks are real cool — or they're magma...

The extrusive igneous rock basalt is made of the same minerals as the intrusive rock <u>gabbro</u> — but gabbro is <u>coarser</u> than basalt because it cools more slowly, giving bigger crystals. It's a case of <u>slow</u>, <u>big</u> and <u>coarse</u> for intrusive rocks versus <u>fast</u>, <u>small</u> and <u>smooth</u> for extrusive rocks — remember that and you'll be onto a winner.

Using Limestone

Calcium carbonate is found in the Earth's crust as marble, chalk and limestone. Limestone's fab for building with, but it ain't all hunky-dory — tearing it out of the ground causes quite a few problems.

Limestone is Used as a Building Material

1) Limestone is a bit of a boring grey/white colour. It's often formed from sea shells and although the original shells are mostly crushed, there are still quite a few fossilised shells remaining.
2) It's quarried out of the ground. This causes some environmental problems though — see below.
3) It's great for making into blocks for building with. Fine old buildings like cathedrals are often made purely from limestone blocks. It's also used for statues and fancy carved bits on nice buildings too.
4) Limestone's virtually insoluble in plain water. But acid rain is a big problem. The acid reacts with the limestone and dissolves it away.
5) Limestone can also be crushed up into chippings and used in road surfacing.

St Paul's Cathedral is made from limestone.

Limestone is Used to Make Other Useful Things Too

1) Limestone is the raw material used to produce other building materials, so it's quarried on a large scale.
2) Powdered limestone is heated in a kiln with powdered clay to make cement.
3) You can then mix the cement with sand, water and gravel to make concrete.
4) And believe it or not — limestone is also used to make glass. You just heat it with sand and sodium carbonate until it melts.

Quarrying Limestone Makes a Right Mess of the Landscape

Digging limestone out of the ground can cause environmental problems.
1) For a start, it makes huge ugly holes which permanently change the landscape.

2) Quarrying processes, like blasting rocks apart with explosives, make lots of noise and dust in quiet, scenic areas.
3) Quarrying destroys the habitats of animals and birds.
4) The limestone needs to be transported away from the quarry — usually in lorries. This causes more noise and pollution.
5) Waste materials produce unsightly tips.

But on the Plus Side...

1) Limestone provides things that people want — like houses and roads. Chemicals used in making dyes, paints and medicines also come from limestone.
2) Limestone products are used to neutralise acidic soil. Acidity in lakes and rivers caused by acid rain is also neutralised by limestone products.
3) Limestone is also used in power station chimneys to neutralise sulfur dioxide, which is a cause of acid rain.
4) The quarry and associated businesses provide jobs for people and bring more money into the local economy. This can lead to local improvements in transport, roads, recreation facilities and health.
5) Once quarrying is complete, landscaping and restoration of the area is normally required as part of the planning permission.

Limestone — a sea creature's cementery...

There's a downside to everything, including using limestone — ripping open huge quarries definitely spoils the countryside. But you have to find a balance — is it worth keeping the countryside pristine if it means loads of people have nowhere to live because there's no stuff available to build houses with?

Limestone and Thermal Decomposition

Limestone and other carbonates get up to some pretty technical reactions — sorry but you've gotta learn 'em.

Limestone *is Mainly* Calcium Carbonate

1) Limestone is mainly <u>calcium carbonate</u> — $CaCO_3$.

2) When it's heated it <u>thermally decomposes</u> to make <u>calcium oxide</u> and <u>carbon dioxide</u>.

> calcium carbonate → calcium oxide + carbon dioxide
> $$CaCO_3 \quad \rightarrow \quad CaO \quad + \quad CO_2$$

Thermal decomposition happens when one substance chemically changes into at least two new substances when it's heated.

3) When <u>other carbonates</u> are heated, they decompose in the <u>same way</u>...

Thermal Decomposition *of* Carbonates *Gives Off* Carbon Dioxide

1) <u>Zinc carbonate</u> and <u>copper carbonate</u> thermally decompose in the same way as calcium carbonate to form an <u>oxide</u> and <u>carbon dioxide</u>.

<u>Heat</u> the carbonate in a boiling tube...

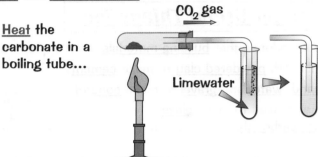

CO_2 gas

Limewater

... and pipe off the gas into a test tube filled with <u>limewater</u> — $Ca(OH)_2$. The CO_2 will turn the limewater <u>milky</u>.

The equations for these reactions are:

> copper carbonate → copper oxide + carbon dioxide
> $$CuCO_3 \quad \rightarrow \quad CuO \quad + \quad CO_2$$

> zinc carbonate → zinc oxide + carbon dioxide
> $$ZnCO_3 \quad \rightarrow \quad ZnO \quad + \quad CO_2$$

2) Some carbonates undergo thermal decomposition more <u>easily</u> than others — it depends on the stability of the metal carbonate.

3) <u>Less stable</u> carbonates will decompose <u>faster</u> and the limewater will turn milky more quickly.

4) Sometimes there's a <u>colour change</u> — e.g. copper carbonate is green and copper oxide is black.

Calcium Oxide *Reacts with* Water *to Produce* Calcium Hydroxide

1) When you <u>add water</u> to calcium oxide you get <u>calcium hydroxide</u>.

> calcium oxide + water → calcium hydroxide   or $CaO + H_2O \rightarrow Ca(OH)_2$

2) Calcium hydroxide is an <u>alkali</u> which can be used to neutralise <u>acidic soil</u> in fields. Powdered calcium oxide can be used for this too, but the <u>advantage</u> of <u>calcium hydroxide</u> is that it works <u>much faster</u>.

3) Calcium hydroxide <u>dissolves</u> in water to produce a solution known as <u>limewater</u> (see above).

Thermal decomposition — *when your vest unravels...*

Limewater isn't actually water with limes dissolved in it. Disappointing isn't it. Its proper name, calcium hydroxide, is much less inspiring. Impress the examiner by remembering the limewater test for carbon dioxide.

Atoms and Mass in Chemical Reactions

Atoms are the main ingredient of chemical reactions and they're only ever <u>rearranged</u> — never lost or made.

Atoms Aren't Lost or Made in Chemical Reactions

1) Elements and compounds are made up of <u>atoms</u> — the <u>smallest</u> particles you can get of each element. It's the atoms that take part in <u>chemical reactions</u>.

2) During chemical reactions, things <u>don't</u> appear out of nowhere and things <u>don't</u> just disappear.

3) You still have the <u>same atoms</u> at the <u>end</u> of a chemical reaction as you had at the <u>start</u>. They're just <u>arranged</u> in different ways to give <u>new products</u> with <u>different properties</u> from the reactants.

4) <u>Balanced symbol equations</u> (see page 48) show the atoms at the <u>start</u> (the <u>reactant</u> atoms) and the atoms at the <u>end</u> (the <u>product atoms</u>) and how they're arranged. For example:

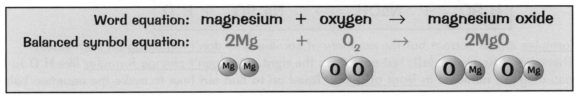

Word equation: magnesium + oxygen → magnesium oxide
Balanced symbol equation: $2Mg$ + O_2 → $2MgO$

5) Because atoms aren't gained or lost, the mass of the reactants <u>equals</u> the mass of the products. So, if you completely react <u>6 g of magnesium</u> with <u>4 g of oxygen</u>, you'd end up with <u>10 g of magnesium oxide</u>.

The Total Mass Before and After a Sealed Reaction is Unchanged

1) If you do a reaction in a <u>sealed</u> container, the <u>total mass</u> before and after <u>doesn't change</u>.

2) A good way of showing this is to do a <u>precipitation</u> reaction.

3) A <u>precipitation</u> reaction happens when <u>two solutions</u> react and an insoluble <u>solid</u> forms in the solution.

4) The solid is said to '<u>precipitate out</u>' and, confusingly, the solid is also called the '<u>precipitate</u>'.

EXAMPLE: <u>Copper sulfate solution</u> reacts with <u>sodium hydroxide</u> to form <u>insoluble copper hydroxide</u>.

$CuSO_4$ + $2NaOH$ → $Cu(OH)_2$ + Na_2SO_4
copper sulfate + sodium hydroxide → copper hydroxide + sodium sulfate

Copper hydroxide is <u>insoluble</u> — so it <u>precipitates out</u>.

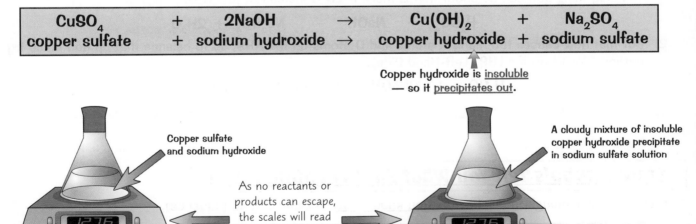

Copper sulfate and sodium hydroxide

As no reactants or products can escape, the scales will read the same throughout the experiment.

A cloudy mixture of insoluble copper hydroxide precipitate in sodium sulfate solution

5) <u>Nothing has escaped</u> from the flask, so the mass at the start and end of the experiment will <u>be the same</u>. No atoms are gained or lost in the reaction, so no mass is gained or lost.

To work out the change in reaction mass...

... just do <u>nothing</u>. As long as your container's sealed, there won't be a change in mass at all. It's all to do with atoms being resistant little blighters. However many you've got at the start of the reaction, you'll have them at the end — unless you let some sneaky gas in, or out, of the system.

Balancing Equations

Equations need a lot of practice if you're going to get them right.
Every time you do an equation you need to practise getting it right rather than skating over it.

Balancing the Equation — Match Them Up One by One

1) There must always be the same number of atoms of each element on both sides — they can't just disappear.

2) You balance the equation by putting numbers in front of the formulas where needed. Take this equation for reacting sulfuric acid (H_2SO_4) with sodium hydroxide (NaOH) to get sodium sulfate (Na_2SO_4) and water (H_2O):

$$H_2SO_4 \ + \ NaOH \ \rightarrow \ Na_2SO_4 \ + H_2O$$

The formulas are all correct but the numbers of some atoms don't match up on both sides. E.g. there are 3 Hs on the left, but only 2 on the right. You can't change formulas like H_2O to H_3O. You can only put numbers in front of them. Read on to find out how to make the equation balance...

Method: Balance Just ONE Type of Atom at a Time

The more you practise, the quicker you get, but all you do is this:

1) Find an element that doesn't balance and pencil in a number to try and sort it out.

2) See where it gets you. It may create another imbalance — if so, just pencil in another number and see where that gets you.

3) Carry on chasing unbalanced elements and it'll sort itself out pretty quickly.

I'll show you. In the equation above you soon notice we're short of H atoms on the RHS (Right-Hand Side).

1) The only thing you can do about that is make it $2H_2O$ instead of just H_2O:

$$H_2SO_4 \ + \ NaOH \ \rightarrow \ Na_2SO_4 \ + 2H_2O$$

2) But that now causes too many H atoms and O atoms on the RHS, so to balance that up you could try putting 2NaOH on the LHS (Left-Hand Side):

$$H_2SO_4 \ + \ 2NaOH \ \rightarrow \ Na_2SO_4 \ + 2H_2O$$

3) And suddenly there it is! Everything balances. And you'll notice the Na just sorted itself out.

State Symbols Tell You What Physical State It's In

These are easy enough, so make sure you know them — especially aq (aqueous).

(s) — Solid	(l) — Liquid	(g) — Gas	(aq) — Dissolved in water

E.g. $\qquad 2Mg_{(s)} \ + \ O_{2(g)} \ \rightarrow \ 2MgO_{(s)}$

Balancing equations — weigh it up in your mind...

REMEMBER WHAT THOSE NUMBERS MEAN:
A number in front of a formula applies to the entire formula. So, $3Na_2SO_4$ means three lots of Na_2SO_4. The little numbers in the middle or at the end of a formula only apply to the atom or brackets immediately before. So the 4 in Na_2SO_4 just means 4 Os, not 4 Ss.

C1a Topic 2 — Materials from the Earth

Revision Summary for C1a Topics 1 & 2

There wasn't anything too ghastly in this section, and a few bits were even quite interesting I reckon. But you've got to make sure the facts are all firmly embedded in your brain and that you really understand the issues. These questions will let you see what you know and what you don't. If you get stuck on any, you need to look at that stuff again. Keep going till you can do them all without coming up for air.

1) Name the two main gases that make up the Earth's atmosphere today.

2) Explain why today's atmosphere is different from the Earth's early atmosphere.

3) How were the oceans formed?

4) List three ways in which human activity is changing the atmosphere.

5) Apart from humans, what else is changing the atmosphere?

6) Describe how you could investigate the proportion of oxygen in the air.

7) Name the three types of rock.

8) What type of rock is marble and how is it formed?

9) What type of rock is chalk?

10) Describe the difference in the way the crystals of extrusive and intrusive rocks form.

11) Name three building materials made from limestone.

12) Plans to develop a limestone quarry and a cement factory on some hills next to your town are announced. Describe the views that the following might have:
    a) dog owners   b) a mother of young children
    c) the owner of a cafe   d) a beetle

13) What is thermal decomposition?

14) Write down the symbol equation showing the thermal decomposition of limestone.

15) How could you test for carbon dioxide in a thermal decomposition reaction?

16) Write down the symbol equation for the thermal decomposition reaction of zinc carbonate.

17) What product can be made by adding water to calcium oxide and why is it useful?

18) Are atoms lost and made in a reaction or just rearranged?

19) If you carry out a reaction in a sealed container, what would you notice about the mass of the reactants and products?

20) What is a precipitate?

21)* Balance these equations: a) $CaCO_3 + HCl \rightarrow CaCl_2 + H_2O + CO_2$

                          b) $Ca + H_2O \rightarrow Ca(OH)_2 + H_2$

22) What does a number in front of a formula apply to?

23) What is the state symbol for 'dissolved in water'?

* Answers on page 108.

C1b Topic 3 — Acids

Hazard Symbols, Acids and Alkalis

Well done, you've made it through to the third Chemistry topic. I hope you had a good journey and didn't get too lost along the way. My name is <u>Ermintrude</u> and I'll be your guide to the world of acids.

You Need to Learn the Common Hazard Symbols

Lots of the chemicals you'll meet in Chemistry can be <u>bad for you</u> or <u>dangerous</u> in some way. That's why the chemical containers will normally have <u>symbols</u> on them to tell you what the dangers are. Understanding these hazard symbols means that you'll be able to use suitable <u>safe-working procedures</u> in the lab.

Oxidising
<u>Provides oxygen</u> which allows other materials to <u>burn more fiercely</u>.
<u>Example:</u> Liquid oxygen.

Highly Flammable
<u>Catches fire</u> easily.
<u>Example:</u> Petrol.

Toxic
<u>Can cause death</u> either by swallowing, breathing in, or absorption through the skin.
<u>Example:</u> Hydrogen cyanide.

Harmful
Like toxic but <u>not quite as dangerous</u>.
<u>Example:</u> Copper sulfate.

Irritant
Not corrosive but <u>can cause reddening or blistering of the skin</u>.
<u>Examples:</u> Bleach, children, etc.

Corrosive
<u>Attacks and destroys living tissues</u>, including eyes and skin.
<u>Example:</u> Concentrated sulfuric acid.

Substances can be Acids, Bases or Neutral

An <u>acid</u> is a substance with a pH less than 7. A <u>base</u> is a substance with a pH greater than 7. An <u>alkali</u> is a base that <u>dissolves in water</u>.

These are the colours you get when you add Universal indicator to an acid or an alkali.

There's a <u>sliding scale</u> from very strong <u>acid</u> to very strong <u>base</u>, with neutral water in the middle.

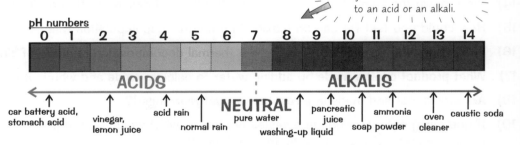

pH numbers
0 1 2 3 4 5 6 7 8 9 10 11 12 13 14

ACIDS   ALKALIS
NEUTRAL

car battery acid, stomach acid | vinegar, lemon juice | acid rain | normal rain | pure water | washing-up liquid | pancreatic juice | soap powder | ammonia | oven cleaner | caustic soda

Neutralisation Reactions Between Acids and Bases Make Salts

An acid and a base <u>react together</u> to form a <u>salt</u> and <u>water</u>. The products of the reaction aren't strongly acidic or alkaline — they're <u>neutral</u>. So it's called a <u>neutralisation reaction</u>.

This is the equation for <u>any neutralisation reaction</u>:

acid + base → salt + water

Neutralisation reactions can be used to make <u>salts</u>, which have a bunch of exciting uses:

1) Salts are used in <u>fertilisers</u> — e.g. ammonium nitrate, ammonium phosphate.
2) Salts are used in <u>fireworks</u> as <u>colouring agents</u> — e.g. calcium chloride (for an orange colour), copper chloride (for a bluey-green colour).

Salt of the earth, of the sea, and of the test tube...

It's amazing the things that salts are used for. Interestingly, some of the same ones used as <u>fertilisers</u> are also very good <u>oxidising agents</u>. They release oxygen, which helps fuels burn — sometimes with a <u>bang</u>, like in fireworks. And that means they're highly likely to have one of those beautiful <u>hazard symbols</u> on them.

Hydrochloric Acid and Indigestion Tablets

You probably don't realise just how much we rely on the power of <u>acids</u> and <u>alkalis</u> — even eating your <u>dinner</u> would be much more difficult without them.

The Stomach Produces Hydrochloric Acid

1) <u>Acids</u> are pretty useful in the <u>human body</u>.

2) The <u>stomach</u> produces <u>hydrochloric acid</u> (HCl) to help with digestion. The enzymes which break down food in the stomach work best in an <u>acidic</u> environment.

3) Having acid in the stomach also helps to kill <u>bacteria</u> — making it less likely that you'll go down with some kind of nasty <u>food poisoning</u>.

4) <u>Indigestion</u> is caused by too much <u>hydrochloric acid</u> in the stomach. Indigestion tablets contain <u>bases</u> such as <u>calcium carbonate</u>, which <u>neutralise</u> the excess acid.

Some Indigestion Remedies are More Effective Than Others

<u>TV adverts</u> are right — some types of <u>indigestion tablets</u> really are more <u>effective</u> than their rivals. There are various <u>experiments</u> you can do to test the effectiveness of tablets. For example, you can test <u>how much acid</u> a single tablet can <u>neutralise</u>. Here's how you could do it:

You need to test <u>at least two different</u> types of indigestion tablet so that you can <u>compare</u> the results. For each type of tablet:

1) Crush up <u>one dose</u> and <u>dissolve</u> it in <u>water</u> in a conical flask. To make sure it's a fair test, you should always use the <u>same volume</u> of water (e.g. 25 cm³) and check that the tablet has <u>completely dissolved</u>.

2) Add three drops of <u>indicator</u> to the conical flask. This will <u>change colour</u> when the solution has been <u>neutralised</u>.

3) Fill a <u>burette</u> (a tall, thin measuring tube with a tap at the bottom) with <u>hydrochloric acid</u>. Make sure you fill it carefully so you know how much acid you've got to begin with.

4) Using the <u>burette</u>, add the <u>acid</u> to the conical flask a bit at a time, giving the conical flask a regular <u>swirl</u>.

5) The <u>end-point</u> is when the colour change <u>lasts</u> rather than disappearing after a few seconds. When you think it's about to be reached, go especially <u>slowly</u> — drip by drip.

6) When the indicator <u>changes colour</u>, all the alkali has been <u>neutralised</u> and you should <u>stop adding acid</u>.

7) <u>Read</u> the burette to work out what volume of acid you've added to the alkali.

8) <u>Repeat</u> the experiment three times for each type of tablet and take an <u>average</u> of the volume of <u>acid</u> needed. This will <u>increase</u> the <u>reliability</u> of your results.

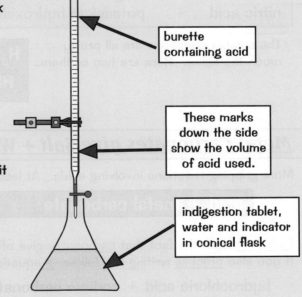

burette containing acid

These marks down the side show the volume of acid used.

indigestion tablet, water and indicator in conical flask

Once you've tested all the tablets, compare the <u>volume of acid</u> required to neutralise each tablet. The <u>most effective</u> tablet is the one which requires the <u>most acid</u> to neutralise it — because it will be able to neutralise the <u>largest</u> amount of acid in the <u>stomach</u>.

Alternatively, you could just eat a really enormous dinner...

You may have studied a different method of testing indigestion tablets in class — if you have, it's up to you which one you learn. Just remember that in the exam you should describe the <u>experiment method</u> — what you would actually <u>measure</u> (e.g. how much, how long) and how you would make sure that the experiment is <u>fair</u>.

Reactions of Acids

Here's more stuff on <u>neutralisation</u> reactions — mixing <u>dilute acids</u> with various <u>bases</u> to make <u>salts</u>.

Metal Oxides <u>and</u> Metal Hydroxides <u>are Often</u> Bases

1) <u>Metal oxides</u> and <u>metal hydroxides</u> are generally <u>bases</u>.
2) This means they can be <u>neutralised with acids</u> to form <u>a salt</u> and <u>water</u>.

acid + metal oxide → salt + water

acid + metal hydroxide → salt + water

The Combination of Metal and Acid Decides the Salt

This isn't exactly exciting but it's pretty easy, so try and get the hang of it:

hydrochloric acid	+	copper oxide	→	copper chloride + water
hydrochloric acid	+	sodium hydroxide	→	sodium chloride + water
sulfuric acid	+	zinc oxide	→	zinc sulfate + water
sulfuric acid	+	calcium hydroxide	→	calcium sulfate + water
nitric acid	+	magnesium oxide	→	magnesium nitrate + water
nitric acid	+	potassium hydroxide	→	potassium nitrate + water

The symbol equations are all pretty much the same. Here are two of them:

$$H_2SO_{4\,(aq)} + ZnO_{(s)} \rightarrow ZnSO_{4\,(aq)} + H_2O_{(l)}$$
$$HNO_{3\,(aq)} + KOH_{(aq)} \rightarrow KNO_{3\,(aq)} + H_2O_{(l)}$$

Metal Carbonates <u>give</u> Salt + Water + Carbon Dioxide

More gripping reactions involving acids. At least there are some <u>bubbles</u> involved here.

acid + metal carbonate → salt + water + carbon dioxide

<u>Definitely</u> learn the fact that <u>carbonates</u> give off <u>carbon dioxide</u> when they neutralise acids.
If you also <u>practise</u> writing the following equations out <u>from memory</u>, it'll do you no harm at all.

hydrochloric acid + sodium carbonate → sodium chloride + water + carbon dioxide

$$2HCl + Na_2CO_3 \rightarrow 2NaCl + H_2O + CO_2$$

Here's another example. (Notice how the equation's quite similar.)

hydrochloric acid + calcium carbonate → calcium chloride + water + carbon dioxide

$$2HCl + CaCO_3 \rightarrow CaCl_2 + H_2O + CO_2$$

Kettle + acid → tea + stomach ache...

The acid + carbonate reaction is one you might have to do at home. If you live in a <u>hard water</u> area, you'll get insoluble $MgCO_3$ and $CaCO_3$ 'furring up' your kettle. You can get rid of this with 'descaler', which is dilute <u>acid</u> (often citric acid) — this reacts with the <u>insoluble carbonates</u> to make <u>soluble salts</u>.

Electrolysis

Hmm, electrolysis. A not-very-catchy title for quite a <u>sparky</u> subject...

Electrolysis Means "<u>Splitting Up with Electricity</u>"

1) <u>Electrolysis</u> is the <u>breaking down</u> (decomposition) of a compound using <u>electrical energy</u>.
2) The electricity used comes from a <u>d.c.</u> (direct current) source, such as a <u>battery</u>.
3) It requires a <u>liquid</u> to <u>conduct</u> the <u>electricity</u>, called the <u>electrolyte</u>.
4) The electricity is applied to the electrolyte by two <u>electrodes</u>.
5) The electrolyte contains the <u>compound</u>, which is broken down into its component parts.
6) The component parts are <u>released</u> as atoms or molecules — often as a <u>gas</u>.

You can <u>Electrolyse Hydrochloric Acid</u>

1) The <u>electrolyte</u> is a dilute <u>solution</u> of hydrochloric acid (HCl).
2) Applying a <u>d.c. current</u> to the electrolyte causes the hydrochloric acid to <u>decompose</u> into its <u>two</u> component parts:

   - <u>hydrogen gas</u> (H_2)   •   <u>chlorine gas</u> (Cl_2)

3) The gases <u>bubble</u> through the solution and can be <u>collected</u> at the <u>electrodes</u>.

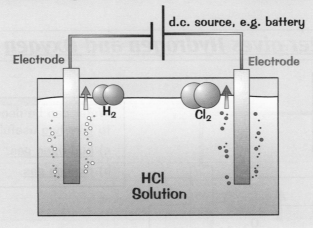

d.c. source, e.g. battery

Electrode   Electrode

H_2 Cl_2

HCl
Solution

You can <u>Test</u> for <u>Chlorine</u> and <u>Hydrogen Gases</u>

Chlorine Chlorine <u>bleaches</u> damp <u>litmus paper</u>, turning it white. (It may turn <u>red</u> for a moment first though — that's because a solution of chlorine is <u>acidic</u>.)

Damp litmus paper

Hydrogen Hydrogen makes a "<u>squeaky pop</u>" with a <u>lighted splint</u>. (The noise comes from the hydrogen burning with the oxygen in the air to form H_2O.)

Squeaky pop!

H_2 gas

Squeaky pop — the reason why you should never squeeze a mouse...

Eek, all this electrolysis stuff can seem a bit complicated at first — so you need to take it <u>slowly</u> and get it <u>clear</u> in your head. Make sure you learn the <u>products</u> of the electrolysis of dilute hydrochloric acid. You also need to be able to explain how to <u>test</u> for chlorine and hydrogen gases.

Electrolysis

Make sure you <u>understand</u> the <u>basics</u> of electrolysis before revising this page. If you're in any <u>doubt</u> go back and revise the <u>previous page</u> again — it'll be worth it, I promise.

Electrolysis of Salt Produces Chlorine

1) <u>Sea water</u> or <u>brine</u> (sodium chloride solution) can be decomposed by <u>electrolysis</u>.
2) This is a really handy way to make <u>chlorine gas</u>.
3) Chlorine gas is <u>toxic</u> — so this makes the manufacture of it a hazardous process.
4) You need to know about <u>three</u> uses of chlorine:

> • it's used to <u>treat water supplies</u> — it kills bacteria and other micro-organisms so that the water's safe to drink.

> • it's needed for the manufacture of <u>bleach</u>.

> • it's used to make the polymer <u>poly(chloroethene)</u> — PVC.

Electrolysis of Water gives Hydrogen and Oxygen

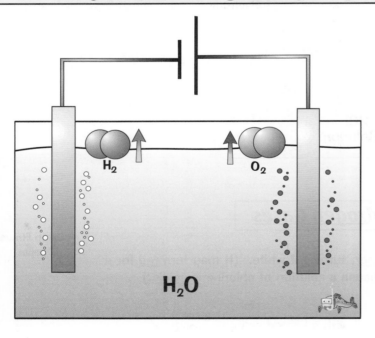

H_2

O_2

H_2O

> Water can be decomposed by electrolysis to give <u>two</u> useful products:
> a) <u>hydrogen gas</u>.
> b) <u>oxygen gas</u>.

> • You can <u>test</u> for oxygen by checking if the gas <u>relights</u> a <u>glowing splint</u>.

Glowing splint

> • Look back to the previous page for the <u>hydrogen test</u>.

Something to do when you're bored at the dinner table...

Chlorine is pretty <u>handy</u> stuff — just think of all the <u>swimming pools</u> around the world that use the stuff. It's not just in swimming pools though, it's also used to treat <u>domestic water supplies</u> — the stuff that comes out of taps has also been chlorinated. Actually, that makes it pretty important stuff for keeping us all <u>healthy</u>. Oh, and well-clothed — the world was a very different place before the invention of the PVC trouser.

Metal Ores

Most metals can't be found as pure lumps. You have to <u>extract</u> them from a <u>compound</u>.

Most Metals are Found in Ores

1) Metals that are <u>unreactive</u> don't tend to form <u>compounds</u> with other elements. Unreactive metals such as <u>gold</u> are found <u>uncombined</u> — so you just have to find them and dig 'em up.

2) However, most metals <u>do react</u> with other elements to form compounds, which can be found naturally in the <u>Earth's crust</u>. If a compound contains enough of the metal to make it <u>worthwhile extracting</u>, the compound is called a <u>metal ore</u>. There's a <u>limited amount</u> of metal ores — they're "<u>finite resources</u>".

3) The <u>more reactive</u> a metal is, the <u>harder it is to extract it from a compound</u>.

Metals Often have to be Separated from their Oxides

1) Lots of common metals, like iron and aluminium, react with <u>oxygen</u> to form <u>oxides</u>. This process is called <u>oxidation</u>. These oxides are often the <u>ores</u> that the metals need to be extracted from.

2) A reaction that separates a metal from its oxide is called a <u>reduction reaction</u>.

FORMATION OF METAL ORE:	EXTRACTION OF METAL:
Oxidation	**Reduction**
Gain of Oxygen	**Loss of Oxygen**
E.g. magnesium is <u>oxidised</u> to make magnesium oxide.	E.g. copper oxide is <u>reduced</u> to copper.
$2Mg + O_2 \longrightarrow 2MgO$	$2CuO + C \longrightarrow 2Cu + CO_2$

3) The most common type of reduction reaction uses <u>carbon</u> to separate the oxygen from the metal, but this doesn't work for all metals...

Methods of Extraction are Linked to the Order of Reactivity

1) Only metals that are <u>less reactive</u> than <u>carbon</u> can be extracted by a reduction reaction with carbon — this is done by <u>heating</u> the ore with <u>carbon</u>.

2) This is because <u>more reactive elements</u> form compounds more <u>readily</u>. Carbon's more reactive than iron, so carbon 'steals' oxygen from iron oxide. Same with zinc, tin and lead.

3) In other words, carbon <u>can only take the oxygen</u> away from metals which are <u>less reactive</u> than carbon <u>itself</u> is.

4) Very reactive metals form very <u>stable</u> ores — i.e. it's difficult to get the metal out of its compound. So metals that are <u>more reactive</u> than carbon (they come <u>higher</u> in the <u>reactivity series</u>) have to be extracted using <u>electrolysis</u>. Electrolysis uses <u>electricity</u> to <u>separate the metal</u> from the other elements in the compound.

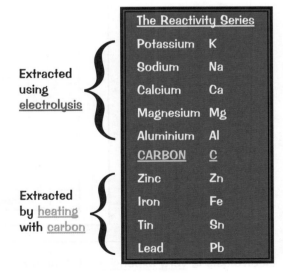

The Reactivity Series	
Potassium	K
Sodium	Na
Calcium	Ca
Magnesium	Mg
Aluminium	Al
<u>CARBON</u>	<u>C</u>
Zinc	Zn
Iron	Fe
Tin	Sn
Lead	Pb

Extracted using <u>electrolysis</u>

Extracted by <u>heating</u> with <u>carbon</u>

Miners — they always have to stick their ore in...

Experiments can tell you where elements are in the <u>reactivity series</u>. E.g. if you can extract a metal from its oxide by reacting it with carbon, then you know that the metal is less reactive than carbon.

Reduction of Metal Ores

The two main methods of metal extraction are <u>reduction using carbon</u> and <u>electrolysis</u>.
OK, neither of them are particularly fascinating but here are some details anyway.

A Lot of Metals can be Extracted From Their Ores Using Carbon

Any metal that is <u>less reactive</u> than carbon can be <u>reduced</u> from its ore using <u>carbon</u> — see previous page.

Iron is <u>lower</u> in the <u>reactivity series</u> than carbon so it can be extracted using carbon, e.g.:

$$2Fe_2O_3 \quad + \quad 3C \quad \rightarrow \quad 4Fe \quad + \quad 3CO_2$$
iron(III) oxide + carbon → iron + carbon dioxide

However, not all metals are less reactive than carbon...

Electrolysis can be Used to Extract Metals

1) <u>Electrolysis</u> is used to extract metals which are higher in the <u>reactivity series</u> than <u>carbon</u> (see previous page).

2) This extraction method <u>breaks down</u> the ores using <u>electricity</u> — see page 53.

3) Here's an <u>example</u> of the way it's used:

Electrolysis Removes Aluminium from its Ore

1) The main ore of aluminium is bauxite, which contains <u>aluminium oxide</u> — Al_2O_3.

2) The aluminium oxide is <u>melted</u> and used as the <u>electrolyte</u> for aluminium extraction.

3) Electrolysis decomposes the aluminium oxide into <u>aluminium</u> and <u>oxygen atoms</u>. The aluminium atoms <u>sink</u> to the bottom of the tank as molten aluminium <u>metal</u>.

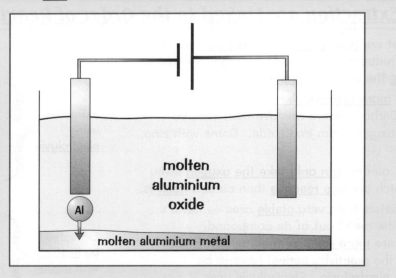

molten
aluminium
oxide

Al

molten aluminium metal

Electrolysis is <u>very expensive</u>. It'll only be used if the metal <u>can't</u> be extracted using reduction with <u>carbon</u>.

Faster shopping at Tesco — use Electrolleys...

Electrolysis is fantastic for removing any unwanted <u>hairs</u> from your body. Great for women with moustaches, or men with hairy backs. And even better for the beauty clinic, as they'll get to charge a small fortune for the treatment. After all, all that electricity makes it a <u>very expensive process</u>...

Properties of Metals

Metals are all the same but slightly different. They have some basic properties in common, but each has its own specific combination of properties, which mean you use different ones for different purposes.

Metals are Strong and Bendy and They're Great Conductors

All metals have some typical properties.

1) Metals are strong (hard to break), but they can be bent or hammered into different shapes.

2) They're great at conducting heat.

3) They conduct electricity well.

Metals have loads of everyday uses because of these properties...

- Their strength and 'bendability' makes them handy for making into things like bridges and car bodies.

- Metals are ideal if you want to make something that heat needs to travel through, like a saucepan base.

- And their electrical conductivity makes them great for making things like electrical wires.

A Metal's Exact Properties Decide How It's Best Used

The properties above are typical properties of metals. Not all metals are the same though — their exact properties determine how they're used. For example:

- Aluminium has a low density and is corrosion-resistant. Pure aluminium isn't particularly strong, but it forms hard, strong alloys (see page 58). These properties make aluminium a very useful structural material. It can be used for loads of things from window frames to electricity cables and aircraft.

- Copper is hard, strong and has a high melting point. It is a good conductor of electricity, so it's ideal for drawing out into electrical wires. It can also be made into pipes, and as it's below hydrogen in the reactivity series, it doesn't react with water. This makes it great for using in plumbing.

- Gold is shiny and extremely easy to shape. It's used for jewellery and in situations where you want a metal that won't react with anything, such as in tooth fillings and in electric circuits.

Some Metals Corrode More Easily Than Others

1) Some metals corrode over time.

2) Corrosion happens because the metal is being oxidised (see page 55).

3) Metals which are high in the reactivity series (see page 55) are more likely to corrode because they react more easily with oxygen. For example, iron is less corrosion-resistant than lead.

For example:

When iron rusts, it's combining with oxygen (and also water). The iron gains oxygen to form iron(III) oxide. Water then becomes loosely bonded to the iron(III) oxide and the result is hydrated iron(III) oxide — which most people call rust.

> iron + oxygen + water → hydrated iron(III) oxide

The word "rust" is only used for the corrosion of iron, not other metals.

Someone robbed your metal? — call a copper...

The Eiffel Tower is made of iron — but as you know, iron goes rusty if air and water get to it. So the Eiffel Tower has to be painted every seven years to make sure that it doesn't rust. This is quite a job and takes an entire year for a team of 25 painters. Too bad they didn't use aluminium. Or concrete.

Making Metals More Useful

Pure metals often aren't quite right for certain jobs. Instead of just making do with what they've got, scientists mix stuff in with the metals to make them exactly how they want.

Pure Iron Tends to be a Bit Too Bendy

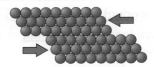

1) 'Iron' extracted in a blast furnace using carbon monoxide is only <u>96% iron</u>. The other 4% is impurities, including <u>carbon</u>.

2) This impure iron is <u>brittle</u>. It's used for <u>ornamental railings</u> but it doesn't have many other uses.

3) So <u>all</u> the impurities are removed from most of the blast furnace iron. This pure iron has a <u>regular arrangement</u> of identical atoms. The layers of atoms can <u>slide over each other</u>, which makes the iron <u>soft</u> and <u>easily shaped</u>. This iron is far <u>too bendy</u> for most uses.

Most Iron is Converted into Steel — an Alloy

An <u>alloy</u> is a mixture of two or more <u>metals</u>, or a mixture of a <u>metal</u> and a <u>non-metal</u>. Most pure iron is changed into <u>alloys</u> called <u>steels</u>. Steels are formed by adding <u>small</u> amounts of <u>carbon</u> and sometimes <u>other metals</u> to the iron. The alloys produced are <u>stronger</u> and more <u>corrosion-resistant</u> (see page 57).

TYPE OF STEEL	PROPERTIES	USES
Low carbon steel (0.1% carbon)	easily shaped	car bodies
High carbon steel (1.5% carbon)	very hard, inflexible	blades for cutting tools, bridges
Stainless steel (chromium added, and sometimes nickel)	rust-resistant	cutlery, containers for corrosive substances

Alloys are Harder Than Pure Metals

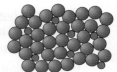

1) Different elements have <u>different sized atoms</u>. So when an element such as carbon is added to pure iron, the <u>smaller</u> carbon atom will <u>upset</u> the layers of pure iron atoms, making it more difficult for them to slide over each other. So alloys are <u>harder</u>.

2) Many metals in use today are actually <u>alloys</u>. E.g.:

> <u>Gold alloys</u> are used to make <u>jewellery</u>. Pure gold is <u>too soft</u> so metals such as zinc, copper and nickel are used to harden it. The <u>proportion</u> of <u>pure gold</u> in an alloy is described by <u>carats</u> or <u>fineness</u>.
> - Pure gold is described as "24 carat", so 18 <u>carats</u> means that 18 out of 24 parts of the alloy are pure gold. In other words, 18 carat gold is 75% gold.
> - <u>Fineness</u> refers to the parts of pure gold per thousand — so 750 fineness is the same as 18 carat gold.

3) Because we understand about the properties of metals, alloys can be <u>designed</u> for specific uses.

Smart Alloys Return to Their Original Shape

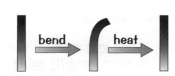
bend → heat →

1) Some smart alloys have a <u>shape memory</u> property — they "<u>remember</u>" their original shape.

2) An example of a smart alloy is <u>nitinol</u>, which is an alloy of <u>nickel</u> and <u>titanium</u>.

3) If you <u>bend</u> a wire made of this smart alloy, it'll go back to its <u>original shape</u> when it's <u>heated</u>.

4) Scientists develop lots of <u>new materials</u>, such as shape memory alloys, to fit <u>new uses</u>. For example, nitinol is handy for things like <u>glasses frames</u> — if they get bent (or sat on) they can easily be reshaped. Shape memory alloys are also used to make <u>stents</u> (tubes) for use in <u>damaged blood vessels</u>.

Not smart enough to do the exam for you though...

Hmm, so scientists can faff about with <u>metals</u> until they can make them do <u>exactly</u> what they want. Well, I'd like a <u>gold ring</u> that can cook meals, do the washing up and tidy rooms. And buy chocolate. Thanks.

Recycling

It's a chemist's job to make sure we have the chemicals we need. But all these chemicals come from the Earth, and the supplies aren't infinite. So we have to think a bit...

It's Important to Recycle Metals

Something we can all do to help is recycle stuff. There are various reasons why.

1 It uses less resources

There's a finite amount of metal in the Earth. Recycling conserves the resources.

2 It uses less energy

Mining and extracting metals needs lots of energy, which mostly comes from burning fossil fuels (which will run out, and which cause pollution). Recycling things like copper and aluminium takes a fraction of the energy.

3 It uses less money

Energy doesn't come cheap, so recycling saves money too.

4 It makes less rubbish

Recycling also cuts down on the amount of rubbish that goes to landfill, which takes up space and pollutes the surroundings.

There May be Economic and Environmental Benefits

1) Working out the economic benefits of recycling can get a bit tricky — there's lots to take into account.
2) For example, recycling isn't free. There are costs involved in collecting waste material, transporting it, sorting it, and then processing it.
3) But if you didn't recycle, say, aluminium, you'd have to mine more aluminium ore — 4 tonnes for every 1 tonne of aluminium you need. But mining makes a mess of the landscape (and these mines are often in rainforests). The ore then needs to be transported, and the aluminium extracted (which uses loads of electricity). And don't forget the cost of sending your used aluminium to landfill.

4) So it's a complex calculation, but for every 1 kg of aluminium cans you recycle, you save:

- 95% or so of the energy needed to mine and extract 'fresh' aluminium,
- 4 kg of aluminium ore,
- a lot of waste.

> In fact, aluminium's about the most cost-effective metal to recycle.

5) But even if all these differences were very small, maybe it's still worth recycling — you're getting people involved in doing their bit for the environment. Can't be a bad thing.

Hard work never killed anyone, but why take a chance...*

You can calculate the financial benefits of recycling any material, but remember there are the 'resources', 'energy' and 'rubbish' benefits too. Not only does recycling aluminium cans reduce the amount of waste from mining, but it also reduces the number of cans heading straight to the landfill. It's a double whammy winner.

Fractional Distillation of Crude Oil

Crude oil is formed from the buried remains of plants and animals — it's a fossil fuel. Over millions of years, with high temperature and pressure, the remains turn to crude oil which is extracted by drilling and pumping.

Crude Oil is a Mixture of Hydrocarbons

1) Crude oil is a mixture of different sized hydrocarbon molecules.

2) Hydrocarbons are basically fuels such as petrol and diesel. They're made of just carbon and hydrogen.

3) Because it's a mixture, the different hydrocarbon molecules aren't chemically bonded to one another — so they all keep their original properties, such as their condensing points.

4) This means that crude oil can be split up into its more useful separate fractions by fractional distillation. Each fraction contains molecules with a similar number of carbon and hydrogen to each other.

Crude Oil is Split into Separate Groups of Hydrocarbons

The fractionating column works continuously, with heated crude oil piped in at the bottom. The vaporised oil rises up the column and the various fractions are constantly tapped off at the different levels where they condense.

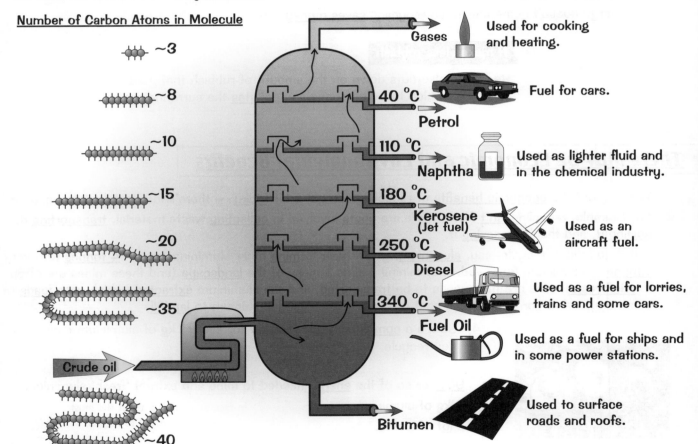

Number of Carbon Atoms in Molecule

~3

~8

~10

~15

~20

~35

Crude oil

~40

Gases — Used for cooking and heating.

40 °C — Petrol — Fuel for cars.

110 °C — Naphtha — Used as lighter fluid and in the chemical industry.

180 °C — Kerosene (Jet fuel) — Used as an aircraft fuel.

250 °C — Diesel — Used as a fuel for lorries, trains and some cars.

340 °C — Fuel Oil — Used as a fuel for ships and in some power stations.

Bitumen — Used to surface roads and roofs.

The shorter the molecules, the more flammable (easier to ignite) the hydrocarbon is.
Also, the shorter the molecules, the more runny the hydrocarbon is — that is, the less viscous (gloopy) it is.

Crude oil — it's always cracking dirty jokes...

It's amazing what you get from buried dead stuff. But it has had a few hundred million years to get into the useful state it's in now. When we burn crude oil fractions, e.g. petrol, kerosene or diesel oil, we're burning up non-renewable fuels — if we use it all, we're going to have to wait an awful long time for more to form. No one knows exactly when oil will run out, but some scientists reckon that it'll only last about another 30 years.

Burning Fuels

We get loads of fuels from oil. And then we burn them. But there's <u>burning</u> and there's <u>burning</u>...

Complete Combustion <u>Happens When There's Plenty of</u> Oxygen

1) When there's <u>plenty of oxygen</u> about, hydrocarbons burn to produce only <u>carbon dioxide</u> and <u>water</u>.

> hydrocarbon + oxygen ⟶ carbon dioxide + water   (+ energy)

2) The <u>hydrogen</u> and <u>carbon</u> in the hydrocarbon have both been <u>oxidised</u>.

3) Many <u>gas room heaters</u> release these <u>waste gases</u> into the room, which is perfectly OK. As long as the gas heater is <u>working properly</u> and the room is <u>well ventilated</u>, there's no problem.

4) <u>Complete combustion</u> releases <u>lots of energy</u> and only produces those two <u>harmless waste products</u>. When there's <u>plenty of oxygen</u> and combustion is complete, the gas burns with a <u>clean blue flame</u>.

5) Here's the <u>equation</u> for the complete combustion of <u>methane</u> — a simple hydrocarbon fuel.

Lots of CO_2 isn't ideal, but the alternatives are worse (see below).

Natural gas is mostly methane (CH_4).

$$CH_4 + 2O_2 \rightarrow 2H_2O + CO_2$$

You can test for CO_2 by bubbling the gas through limewater. It turns limewater milky (see page 46).

Incomplete Combustion <u>of Hydrocarbons is</u> NOT Safe

1) If there <u>isn't enough oxygen</u> the combustion will be <u>incomplete</u>. Carbon dioxide and water are still produced, but you can also get <u>carbon monoxide</u> (CO) and <u>carbon</u>.

2) Incomplete combustion means a <u>smoky yellow flame</u>, and <u>less energy</u> than complete combustion.

> hydrocarbon + oxygen ⟹ carbon + carbon monoxide + carbon dioxide + water   (+ energy)

3) The <u>carbon monoxide</u> is a <u>colourless</u>, <u>odourless</u> and very toxic (<u>poisonous</u>) gas.

4) Every year people are <u>killed</u> while they sleep due to <u>faulty</u> gas fires and boilers filling the room with <u>carbon monoxide</u> and nobody realising — this is why it's important to <u>regularly service gas appliances</u>. The black carbon given off produces <u>sooty marks</u> — a <u>clue</u> that the fuel is <u>not</u> burning fully.

5) So basically, you want <u>lots of oxygen</u> when you're burning fuel — you get <u>more energy</u> given out, and you don't get any <u>messy soot</u> or <u>poisonous gases</u>.

6) Here's an example of an <u>equation</u> for incomplete combustion too.

$$4CH_4 + 6O_2 \rightarrow C + 2CO + CO_2 + 8H_2O$$

This is just <u>one possibility</u>. The products depend on how much oxygen is present... ... e.g. you could also have: $4CH_4 + 7O_2 \rightarrow 2CO + 2CO_2 + 8H_2O$ — the important thing is that the equation is <u>balanced</u> (see p.48).

There's Lots to Consider When <u>Choosing the</u> Best Fuel

1) <u>Ease of ignition</u> — whether it <u>burns easily</u>. Fuels like gas burn more easily than diesel.

2) <u>Energy value</u> (i.e. amount of energy released) — see page 66 for more on this.

3) <u>Ash and smoke</u> — some fuels, like coal, leave behind a lot of <u>ash</u> that needs to be disposed of.

4) <u>Storage and transport</u> — gas needs to be stored in special <u>canisters</u> and coal needs to be kept <u>dry</u>. Fuels need to be transported <u>carefully</u> as gas leaks and oil spills can be dangerous.

Blue flame good, orange flame bad...

An ideal fuel would be <u>easy to ignite</u>, produce <u>no soot</u> or <u>toxic products</u>, release <u>loads of energy</u>, leave no <u>residue</u> (what's left after burning), and be capable of being <u>stored safely</u>. There should also be a <u>cheap</u> and <u>sustainable supply</u> of it. In reality, you have to go for the <u>best compromise</u>.

Environmental Problems

Remember crude oil (page 60) — 90% of it is used as fuel. It's burnt to release the energy stored inside it.

Burning Fuels Releases Gases and Particles

1) Power stations burn huge amounts of fossil fuels to make electricity.
   Cars are also a major culprit in burning fossil fuels.

2) When fossil fuels are burnt, carbon dioxide and water vapour are always released into the atmosphere.

   > hydrocarbon + oxygen → carbon dioxide + water vapour

3) Sulfur impurities are found in petrol and diesel so sulfur dioxide is also put into the air.

4) If there's not enough oxygen for the fuel to burn properly, particles of soot (carbon) and carbon monoxide are also released.

Sulfur Dioxide Causes Acid Rain

1) Sulfur dioxide is one of the gases that causes acid rain.

2) When the sulfur dioxide mixes with clouds it forms dilute sulfuric acid. This then falls as acid rain.

3) Acid rain causes lakes to become acidic and many plants and animals die as a result.

4) Acid rain kills trees and damages limestone buildings and ruins stone statues. It's shocking.

5) Links between acid rain and human health problems have been suggested.

6) The benefits of electricity and travel have to be balanced against the environmental impacts. Governments have recognised the importance of this and international agreements have been put in place to reduce emissions of air pollutants such as sulfur dioxide.

Sulfur can be Removed From Fuels Before They're Burned

1) Most of the sulfur can be removed from fuels before they are burnt, but it costs more to do it.

2) Also, removing sulfur from fuels takes more energy. This usually comes from burning more fuel, which releases more of the greenhouse gas carbon dioxide.

3) However, petrol and diesel are starting to be replaced by low-sulfur versions.

Acid Rain is Prevented by Cleaning Up Emissions

1) Power stations now have Acid Gas Scrubbers to take the harmful gases out before they release their fumes into the atmosphere. (These use limestone — see page 45.)

2) Most cars are now fitted with catalytic converters to clean up their exhaust gases.

3) The other way of reducing acid rain is simply to reduce our usage of fossil fuels.

Eee, problems, problems — there's always summat goin' wrong...

Pollutants like sulfur dioxide can be carried a long way in the atmosphere. So a country might suffer from acid rain that it didn't cause, which doesn't seem very fair. It's not just up to big industries though — there's lots of things you can do to reduce the amount of fossil fuels burnt. Putting an extra jumper on instead of turning up the heating helps. As does walking places instead of cadging a lift.

More Environmental Problems

From driving around in gas guzzlers to lopping down trees, we're messing with natural CO_2 levels.

Carbon Dioxide is a Greenhouse Gas

1) The <u>temperature</u> of the Earth is a <u>balance</u> between the heat it gets from the Sun and the heat it radiates back out into space.

2) Gases in the <u>atmosphere</u> like <u>carbon dioxide</u>, <u>methane</u> and <u>water vapour</u> naturally act like an <u>insulating layer</u>. They are often called 'greenhouse gases'. They absorb most of the heat that would normally be radiated out into space, and re-radiate it in all directions — including back towards the Earth.

3) <u>Human activity</u> affects the <u>amount of greenhouse gases</u> in the atmosphere, e.g. deforestation (see below).

4) The Earth is gradually <u>heating up</u> (global warming). There's a <u>correlation</u> between this and the amount of carbon dioxide in the atmosphere. Although the Earth's temperature <u>varies</u> naturally, there's a <u>scientific consensus</u> that human activity is influencing this and causing <u>climate change</u>.

Human Activity Affects Carbon Dioxide Levels

1) People around the world are <u>cutting down</u> large areas of forest (<u>deforestation</u>) for <u>timber</u> and to clear land for <u>farming</u>. This increases the <u>level of carbon dioxide</u> in the <u>atmosphere</u> because:

- Carbon dioxide is <u>released</u> when trees are <u>burnt</u> to clear land. (Carbon in wood is 'locked up' and doesn't contribute to atmospheric CO_2 — until it's released by burning.)

- <u>Microorganisms</u> feeding on bits of <u>dead wood</u> release CO_2 as a waste product of <u>respiration</u>.

- Because living trees use CO_2 for <u>photosynthesis</u>, removing these trees means <u>less</u> CO_2 is removed from the atmosphere.

So more CO_2 is being put into the atmosphere and less is being taken out.

2) <u>Burning fossil fuels</u> is another way humans are <u>releasing</u> 'locked up' carbon into the <u>atmosphere</u> as CO_2. The carbon was locked up in the fossil fuels when plants and animals were <u>crushed</u> over millions of years.

3) Scientists have been researching ways to <u>restore the balance</u> and <u>limit</u> the increase in CO_2 level in the atmosphere...

Iron Seeding

1) <u>Iron</u> is an element needed by plants for <u>photosynthesis</u>. Injecting iron into the upper ocean promotes the growth of <u>phytoplankton</u>.

2) These <u>blooms</u> of phytoplankton <u>absorb</u> CO_2 from the atmosphere for <u>photosynthesis</u>. This could help to get things back in balance.

3) It's a great idea in theory, only we have no way of controlling what plankton grows — some are <u>toxic</u>. Also, microorganisms which decompose dead plankton use up oxygen and this creates '<u>dead zones</u>' in the ocean — where nothing can live.

Converting Carbon Dioxide into Hydrocarbons

1) Chemists are researching the possibility of <u>converting</u> waste CO_2 into <u>hydrocarbons</u>.

2) Several different methods are being tested — most use <u>high pressure</u>, <u>high temperature</u> and a <u>metal catalyst</u>. <u>Short chain</u> hydrocarbons can be generated fairly <u>easily</u> but the <u>longer</u> hydrocarbons required for petrol are more <u>difficult</u> to produce.

3) This would make a <u>dent</u> in the excess of CO_2, but only if the conversion process used '<u>green</u>' energy.

It's a threat to the Earth as we know it...

The possible consequences of global warming are <u>pretty scary</u>. Maybe colonising Mars isn't such a crazy idea. We might be coming up with some clever ideas to sort things out, but we need to be sure that we don't just end up making things <u>worse</u>. Toxic tides of algae and skinny dipping don't really go together. Sigh.

Biofuels

Nowadays, there are some decent alternatives to fossil fuels on the horizon — biofuels. Biofuels are great because they're made from chemicals obtained from living things. There are two main ones — biogas and ethanol.

Biogas *is Made by* Microorganisms

1) Microorganisms are used to decompose living organisms' waste or dead plants to create biogas, which can be used as fuel.

2) Biogas can be burned to heat water, or used in central heating systems. Or it can power a turbine, which can be used to generate electricity — this is especially useful for producing electricity in remote areas with no mains supply. Biogas can also be used as a fuel for cars and buses.

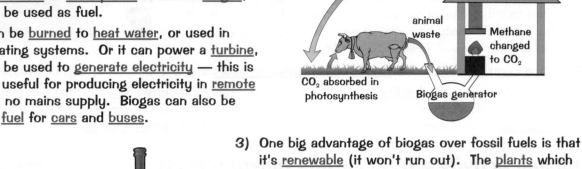

3) One big advantage of biogas over fossil fuels is that it's renewable (it won't run out). The plants which are decomposed to make biogas can be replaced quickly with new crops.

4) Another advantage is that the dead plants needed to make biogas photosynthesised when alive, removing CO_2 from the atmosphere. This balances out the release of CO_2 from burning the biogas.

5) Biogas is a fairly clean fuel — it doesn't produce many particulates (small particles), or significant amounts of sulfur dioxide and oxides of nitrogen (which can cause acid rain — see page 62).

6) Also, the raw materials for biogas (plant waste or manure) are cheap and readily available.

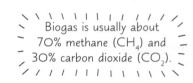
Biogas is usually about 70% methane (CH_4) and 30% carbon dioxide (CO_2).

Alcohol *is Made From* Sugar

1) Ethanol (a type of alcohol) can be used as fuel. It burns to give just CO_2 and water.

2) It can be produced by using yeast to ferment sugars. Materials like sugar cane and sugar beet can be used as a source of sugar in ethanol production.

3) Cars can be adapted to run on a mixture of about 10% ethanol and 90% petrol — 'gasohol'. Some countries (e.g. Brazil) make extensive use of gasohol. It's best used in areas where there's plenty of fertile land for growing the crops needed, and good crop-growing weather.

4) However, because large amounts of land are needed to grow the crops used to produce ethanol, there would be less land available to grow food.

5) Using gasohol instead of pure petrol means that less crude oil is being used. Another advantage is the crops needed for ethanol production absorb CO_2 from the atmosphere in photosynthesis while growing. This goes some way towards balancing out the release of CO_2 when the gasohol is burnt.

6) But distilling the ethanol after fermentation needs a lot of energy, so it's not a perfect solution.

Do your bit for the environment — buy a cow...

These energy sources sound great — but you have to think. E.g. biogas might sound like a cheap and easy fuel paradise, but you have to remember there are pros and cons. While the CO_2 produced by burning the fuel balances out the CO_2 that's removed from the atmosphere by growing the crops, you also have to factor in the CO_2 produced by transporting it. So, you need to look at the whole picture. It's a tricky old game, this.

Fuel Cells

Fuel cells are great — they use hydrogen and oxygen to make electricity.

Hydrogen and Oxygen Give Out Energy When They React

Remember the lab tests for hydrogen and oxygen. Hydrogen plus a lighted splint gives that good old squeaky pop. Oxygen relights a glowing splint.

1) Hydrogen and oxygen react to produce water — which isn't a pollutant.
2) The reaction between hydrogen and oxygen releases energy.
3) Put these two facts together, and you get something useful: you can get energy by reacting hydrogen and oxygen — and it doesn't produce any nasty pollutants, only nice clean water...

Fuel Cells Use Fuel and Oxygen to Produce Electrical Energy

A fuel cell is an electrical cell that's supplied with a fuel and oxygen and uses energy from the reaction between them to generate electricity.

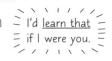

I'd learn that if I were you.

1) Fuel cells were developed in the 1960s as part of the space programme, to provide electrical power on spacecraft — they were more practical than solar cells and safer than nuclear power.
2) Unlike a battery, a fuel cell doesn't run down or need recharging from the mains. It'll produce energy in the form of electricity and heat as long as fuel is supplied.

Hydrogen-Oxygen Fuel Cells Have Lots of Advantages

1) Hydrogen fuel cells are great — they're much more efficient than power stations or batteries at producing electricity. If you use the heat produced as well, their efficiency can be greater than 80%.
2) In a fuel cell, the electricity is generated directly from the reaction (so no turbines, generators, etc.).
3) Because there aren't a lot of stages to the process of generating electricity there are fewer places for energy to be lost as heat.
4) Unlike a car engine or a fossil fuel burning power station, there are no moving parts, so energy isn't lost through friction.

5) Fuel cell vehicles don't produce any conventional pollutants — no greenhouse gases, no nitrogen oxides, no sulfur dioxide, no carbon monoxide. The only by-products are water and heat. This would be a major advantage in cities, where air pollution from traffic is a big problem.

> This could mean no more smelly petrol and diesel cars, lorries and buses.
>
> It could also replace batteries — which are incredibly polluting to dispose of because they're usually made of highly toxic metal compounds.
>
> However, it's not likely to mean the end of either conventional power stations or our dependence on fossil fuels. That's because:
> * hydrogen is a gas so it takes up loads more space to store than liquid fuels like petrol.
> * it's very explosive so it's difficult to store safely.
> * the hydrogen fuel is often made either from hydrocarbons (from fossil fuels), or by electrolysis of water, which uses electricity (and that electricity's got to be generated somehow — usually this involves fossil fuels).

Fuel cells — they're simply electrifying...

These fuel cells sound great — but don't go thinking they're perfect. Once you've got the hydrogen, yeah, fuel cells are ace. But producing that hydrogen takes a lot of energy (usually from burning fossil fuels). That doesn't mean fuel cells won't be more important in the future — only that they're no magic solution.

Measuring the Energy Content of Fuels

Different fuels give out different amounts of energy when they burn. One way to measure the energy content of fuels is by using a none-too-fancy copper cup (or a "calorimeter", to give it its proper name).

You Can Calculate Energy Content by Heating Water

1) This "calorimetric" experiment involves heating water by burning a liquid fuel.

2) If you measure (i) how much fuel you've burned and (ii) the temperature change of the water, you can work out how much energy is supplied by each gram of fuel.

3) You find the mass of fuel burned by subtracting the final mass of fuel and burner from the initial mass of fuel and burner. Simple.

MASS OF FUEL BURNED	=	INITIAL MASS OF FUEL AND BURNER	−	FINAL MASS OF FUEL AND BURNER

4) If you do the same experiment with different fuels, you can compare their energy content. If a fuel has a higher energy content per gram, you need less fuel to cause the same temperature rise.

Calorimetric Method — Reduce Heat Loss as Much as Possible

1) It's dead important to make as much heat as possible go into heating up the water. Reducing draughts is the key here — use a screen to act as a draught excluder (and don't do it next to an open window).

2) Put some fuel into a spirit burner (or use a bottled gas burner if the fuel is a gas) and weigh the burner full of fuel.

3) Measure out, say, 200 cm³ of water into a copper calorimeter.

4) Take the initial temperature of the water — then put the burner under the calorimeter and light the wick.

5) While the water's heating up, stir it every now and then to distribute the heat evenly.

6) When the heat from the burner has made the water temperature rise by 20-30 °C, blow out the spirit burner and make a note of the highest temperature the water reaches.

7) Reweigh the burner and fuel.

8) If you're comparing two fuels, repeat the procedure with the second fuel.

Draught excluder

Insulating lid to reduce heat loss

Copper calorimeter

Thermometer

Spirit burner

Make It a Fair Comparison by Keeping Conditions the Same

1) To compare the energy content of different fuels you need to do the same experiment several times, but using a different fuel in the burner each time.

2) For the comparison to be fair, everything (except the fuel used) should be the same.

3) This means that:

(i) you should use the same apparatus,
(ii) you should use the same amount of water each time,
(iii) the water should start and finish at the same temperature each time.

Hope you've got the energy to revise all this...

In the exam you might need to explain how you could compare the energy content of different fuels. You'll need to give plenty of detail — a wishy-washy answer just won't do. Hmmm, better get learning this page then.

Alkanes and Alkenes

When you crack crude oil (next page) you get <u>alkanes</u> and <u>alkenes</u>. Know the differences between them.

ALKANES Have All C–C SINGLE Bonds

1) They're made up of <u>chains</u> of carbon atoms with <u>single</u> bonds between them.

2) They're called <u>saturated</u> hydrocarbons because they have <u>no</u> spare bonds.

3) This is also why they <u>don't</u> turn <u>bromine water</u> colourless — <u>no</u> spare bonds.

4) They <u>won't</u> form polymers (see page 69) — same reason again, <u>no</u> spare bonds.

5) The first three alkanes are <u>methane</u> (a non-renewable fossil fuel found in natural gas), <u>ethane</u> and <u>propane</u>. Here are their <u>structures</u>:

Bromine water + alkane — still brown.

1) Methane
Formula: CH_4

H
|
H–C–H   (found in
| natural gas)
H

2) Ethane
Formula: C_2H_6

H H
| |
H–C–C–H
| |
H H

3) Propane
Formula: C_3H_8

H H H
| | |
H–C–C–C–H
| | |
H H H

ALKENES Have a C=C DOUBLE Bond

1) They're <u>chains</u> of carbon atoms with one or more <u>double</u> bonds.

2) They are called <u>unsaturated</u> hydrocarbons because they have some 'spare' bonds left.

3) This is why they will decolourise <u>bromine water</u>. They form <u>bonds</u> with bromine atoms.

4) They form <u>polymers</u> by <u>opening up</u> their double bonds to 'hold hands' in a long chain.

5) The first two alkenes are <u>ethene</u> and <u>propene</u>.

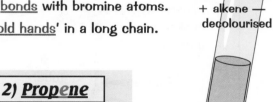

Bromine water + alkene — decolourised

1) Ethene
Formula: C_2H_4

H   H
 \   /
  C = C
 /   \
H   H

2) Propene
Formula: C_3H_6

H H
| | H
H–C–C = C
| | \
H   H

Notice the names:

- "<u>meth-</u>" means "<u>one</u> carbon atom",
- "<u>eth-</u>" means "<u>two</u> C atoms",
- "<u>prop-</u>" means "<u>three</u> C atoms", etc.

The only difference then between the names of <u>alkanes</u> and <u>alkenes</u> is just the "<u>-ane</u>" or "<u>-ene</u>" on the end.

Alkane anybody who doesn't learn this lot properly...

Don't get alkanes confused with alk<u>e</u>nes — that one letter makes all the difference. Alkenes have a C=C bond, alkanes don't. Try using this sentence to help you remember, 'James Double Bond was <u>keen</u> on self defence and gadgets and definitely wouldn't let anyone <u>cane</u> him' — so double bonds must be in alk<u>e</u>nes not alk<u>a</u>nes. The first part of their names are the same though and tell you how many carbon atoms there are in the chain.

Cracking Hydrocarbons

After the distillation of crude oil, you've still got both short and long hydrocarbons, just not all mixed together. But there's <u>more demand</u> for some products, like <u>petrol</u>, than for others.

Cracking — Splitting Up Long-Chain Hydrocarbons

1) <u>Long-chain</u> hydrocarbons form <u>thick</u> gloopy liquids like <u>tar</u> which aren't all that useful.

2) The process called <u>cracking</u> turns them into <u>shorter</u> molecules which are <u>much</u> more useful.

3) <u>Cracking</u> is a form of <u>thermal decomposition</u>, which just means <u>breaking</u> molecules down into <u>simpler</u> molecules by <u>heating</u> them.

4) A lot of the longer molecules produced from fractional distillation are <u>cracked</u> into smaller ones because there's <u>more demand</u> for products like <u>petrol</u> than for diesel or lubricating oil.

5) More importantly, cracking produces <u>alkenes</u>, which are needed for making <u>plastics</u>.

Conditions for Cracking: Heat, Plus a Catalyst

In industry, <u>vaporised hydrocarbons</u> are passed over a <u>powdered catalyst</u> at about <u>400 °C – 700 °C</u>. <u>Silicon dioxide</u> (SiO_2) and <u>aluminium oxide</u> (Al_2O_3) are used as <u>catalysts</u>.

In the lab, you can use <u>porcelain</u> as a catalyst for the reaction:

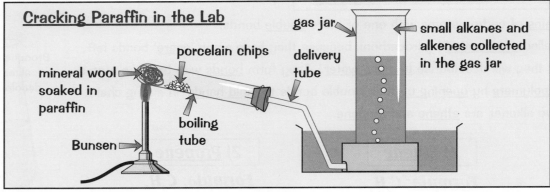

Cracking Paraffin in the Lab

1) Start by <u>heating</u> the <u>paraffin</u>. After a few seconds, <u>move</u> the Bunsen burner to heat the <u>porcelain chips</u>. <u>Alternate</u> between the two until the paraffin <u>vaporises</u> and the porcelain <u>glows red</u>.

2) The heated paraffin vapour <u>cracks</u> as it passes over the heated <u>porcelain</u>.

3) The <u>smaller alkanes and alkenes</u> travel down the delivery tube.

4) The <u>smallest</u> alkanes and alkenes are gases which collect in the <u>gas jar</u>.

5) You can <u>show</u> that the gas in the gas jar contains <u>alkenes</u> because it decolourises <u>bromine water</u> (p.67).

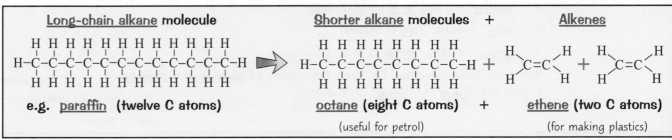

Bunsen and a boiling tube — cracking paraffin-alia...

So, cracking's useful for <u>two things</u> — making alkenes for plastics, and turning bitumen and candle wax (of limited use) into things like petrol and cooking gas (which are really rather handy). Learn that apparatus, and the method for cracking paraffin. Cover the page, scribble it all down, check, try again...

Using Alkenes to Make Polymers

Before we knew how to make <u>polymers</u>, there were no <u>polythene bags</u>. Everyone used string bags for their shopping. Now we have plastic bags that hurt your hands and split halfway home.

Alkenes Can Be Used to Make Polymers

1) Probably the most useful thing you can do with alkenes is <u>polymerisation</u>. This means joining together lots of <u>monomers</u> (small molecules, e.g. alkenes) to form <u>very large molecules</u> — these long-chain molecules are called <u>polymers</u>.

2) For instance, many <u>ethene</u> molecules can be joined up to produce <u>poly(ethene)</u> or "polythene". Remember that the molecules form <u>polymers</u> by <u>opening up</u> their double bonds (see page 67).

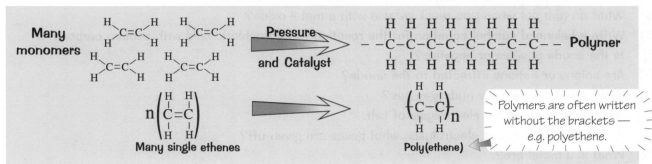

3) Poly(ethene) is <u>stretchy</u> and <u>light</u> so it has loads of uses from <u>plastic bags</u> to <u>hose pipes</u> to <u>laminating</u> paper.

4) In the same way, if you join lots of <u>propene</u> molecules together, you've got <u>poly(propene)</u>. Poly(propene) is <u>tough</u> but <u>flexible</u>. It's used for all sorts of things, from <u>thermal underwear</u> and <u>carpets</u> to <u>plastic containers</u>.

5) Joining lots of <u>chloroethene</u> molecules together gives you <u>poly(chloroethene)</u>, also known as <u>PVC</u>. It's <u>flexible</u> and <u>resistant to wear</u>, so it has many uses — for example, <u>clothing</u>, <u>electric cables</u> and <u>pipes</u>.

6) <u>Tetrafluoroethene</u> polymerises to become <u>poly(tetrafluoroethene)</u> — which is also called <u>PTFE</u> if you're not a fan of tongue twisters. It's <u>unreactive</u>, <u>flame resistant</u> and very <u>resistant to wear</u>, so it's used as a <u>non-stick</u> coating for pans — you've probably heard of it as Teflon®.

Most Plastics Don't Rot, so They're Hard to Get Rid Of

1) Most plastics are '<u>non-biodegradable</u>' — they're not broken down by <u>microorganisms</u>, so they <u>don't rot</u>. If you <u>bury</u> them in a landfill site, they'll still be there <u>years later</u>.

2) When you <u>burn</u> some plastics, they give off <u>toxic gases</u> — that's not a good idea.

3) It's best to <u>recycle</u> them as this helps to <u>conserve resources</u>. There are lots of different <u>types</u> of plastic, so the ones which can be recycled have to be <u>separated</u> from the others first — this makes recycling <u>expensive</u> and <u>difficult</u> though.

4) Developing biodegradable polymers will help with the problems associated with disposing of them:

   • Some polythene bags are now made with <u>starch granules</u> in them. If the plastic is buried, the starch is broken down by microorganisms in the soil, and the bag breaks up into tiny pieces of polythene.

   • You can also get plastics that break down in <u>sunlight</u> — they tend to be used in agriculture.

Revision's like a polymer — you join lots of little facts up...

Polymers are <u>all over the place</u> — and I don't just mean all those plastic bags stuck in trees. There are <u>naturally occurring</u> polymers, like rubber and silk. That's quite a few clothing options, even without synthetic polymers like polyester and PVC. You've even got polymers <u>on the inside</u> — DNA's a polymer.

Revision Summary for C1b Topics 3, 4 & 5

Woah, a bumper crop of questions for all three topics in Unit C1b. Don't worry, this probably isn't the most exciting thing that'll ever happen to you. At least I hope not, for your sake. Anyway, whether you find the topics easy or hard, interesting or dull, you need to learn it all before the exam. Try these questions and see how much you really know:

1) Give the meaning of this symbol: ☠
2) Do acids have a pH greater or less than 7?
3) Name the acid produced by the stomach.
4) How do indigestion tablets work?
5) What do you get when you react an acid with a metal oxide?
6) Write a balanced symbol equation for the reaction of hydrochloric acid with sodium carbonate.
7) Is the anode positive or negative?
8) Are anions or cations attracted to the anode?
9) How would you test for hydrogen gas?
10) Name a product of the electrolysis of salt.
11) When water undergoes electrolysis, what gases are given off?
12) What is a metal ore?
13) Explain the difference between oxidation and reduction.
14) Name two ways in which metals are often extracted from their ores.
15) What is bauxite?
16) Metals are used for car bodies, saucepan bases and electrical wires. For each of these uses, give one reason why metals are appropriate.
17) Why are metals high in the reactivity series more likely to corrode?
18) What is the problem with using a) iron straight from the blast furnace, b) very pure iron?
19) Why are alloys harder than pure metals? Give two examples of alloys and say what's in them.
20) What's so clever about smart alloys?
21) Give three reasons why it's good to recycle metal.
22) What does crude oil consist of? What does fractional distillation do to crude oil?
23) What is produced during complete combustion of hydrocarbons?
24) Explain how incomplete combustion can be harmful to humans.
25) Give four things you might want to consider when deciding on the best fuel to use.
26) What problems are associated with acid rain?
27) List three ways of reducing acid rain.
28) What are greenhouse gases?
29) List two ways in which human activity is increasing CO_2 levels.
30) What are "biofuels"?
31) What are the reactants and products in a fuel cell?
32) List one advantage and one disadvantage of fuel cells.
33) What is a calorimeter?
34) Say whether alkanes and alkenes have double or single bonds. How would you would test this?
35) Draw the structure of the first two alkenes. Then name them.
36) Draw the apparatus used to crack paraffin in the lab.
37) What is a monomer? What is a polymer?
38) Write out the equation for the polymerisation of ethene.
39) Describe some of the problems associated with disposing of plastics.

Changing Ideas About the Solar System

Our Solar System is made up of a <u>star</u> (<u>the Sun</u>) and lots of stuff <u>orbiting</u> it in <u>slightly elongated</u> circles (called ellipses). But <u>scientists</u> and <u>astronomers</u> didn't always think the universe and our Solar System was like that...

Ancient Greeks <u>Thought the Earth</u> <u>was the Centre of the Universe</u>

1) Most ancient Greek astronomers believed that the Sun, Moon, planets and stars all <u>orbited the Earth</u> in perfect <u>circles</u> — this is known as the <u>geocentric model</u>.

2) The <u>geocentric model</u> was the accepted model of the universe from the time of the <u>ancient Greeks</u> until the 1500s. It was only in the 1600s that it began to be replaced by the <u>heliocentric model</u>.

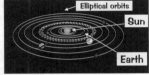
The geocentric model.

The heliocentric model.

3) The <u>heliocentric model</u> states that the Earth and planets all <u>orbit the Sun</u>, which is at the <u>centre</u> of the universe.

4) The heliocentric idea had already been around for 2000 years, but the <u>model</u> was first introduced in a book by <u>Copernicus</u> in 1543. This book showed astronomical observations could be explained <u>without</u> having the <u>Earth</u> at the centre of the universe.

5) Copernicus' ideas <u>weren't</u> popular at the time, and the model itself was condemned by the <u>Church</u>. One of the most convincing pieces of evidence for this theory was <u>Galileo's observations</u> of Jupiter's moons.

In 1610, Galileo was observing Jupiter using a <u>telescope</u> (a <u>new invention</u> at the time) when he saw <u>three stars</u> in a line near the planet. When he looked again the next evening, he saw these stars had moved in the <u>wrong</u> direction in the night sky. After a week, a <u>fourth</u> star appeared. These stars <u>never</u> moved away from Jupiter and seemed to be <u>carried along</u> with the planet — he realised these four objects weren't stars, but <u>moons orbiting Jupiter</u>. This showed <u>not everything</u> was in orbit around the Earth — which proved the geocentric model was <u>wrong</u>.

6) The current model still says that the planets in our Solar System <u>orbit</u> the Sun (see p.82) — but that these orbits are actually <u>elliptical</u> rather than circular.

7) As <u>technology</u> has improved, our idea of the <u>Solar System</u> and the universe has changed. E.g. the invention of the <u>telescope</u> led to the discovery of <u>Uranus</u>.

Our current view of the Solar System.

Visible Light <u>Can Tell Us a Lot About the</u> Universe

1) Most of the stuff <u>scientists</u> know about the <u>universe</u> comes from <u>detecting waves</u> from objects in space. Some objects like stars are <u>huge</u>, very <u>hot</u> and very <u>far away</u> from us. They <u>give out</u> lots of <u>visible light</u> — which is why you can see them, even though they're very far away. We can see the <u>planets</u> in our Solar System because they <u>reflect</u> sunlight.

2) Early astronomers made observations of the universe just using the <u>naked eye</u>. Many very <u>important discoveries</u> of <u>stars</u>, <u>comets</u> and <u>planets</u> were made this way. Most astronomical objects are so <u>far away</u> and look so small that naked eye observations are only really useful for <u>mapping</u> their positions.

3) <u>Telescopes</u> magnify images, so distant objects can be seen in <u>more detail</u>. You can also see objects that are at <u>larger</u> distances. Many new objects have been discovered using telescopes and they've helped us <u>learn more</u> about what the universe is <u>made up</u> of. Telescopes on Earth have problems though (p.84). <u>Space telescopes</u> overcome these issues — but they're <u>expensive</u>.

4) <u>Photographs</u> of the universe can be taken using <u>telescopes</u> — this allows you to '<u>zoom in</u>' and look at objects in <u>more detail</u>. It makes it easier to <u>monitor</u> an object by taking pictures at different <u>times</u> to compare them, and to <u>share</u> your observations with others. You can also see faint objects by allowing a <u>long exposure time</u> so you collect more light — which obviously <u>can't</u> be done with just the naked eye.

Make a model, prove it wrong, make a model, prove it wrong...

It's taken <u>thousands</u> of years for us to reach our <u>current model</u> of the Solar System. Although the geocentric and heliocentric models turned out to be wrong, they played a <u>really important part</u> in helping us reach the model we have today. And unsurprisingly, there's <u>loads</u> that scientists <u>still</u> don't know about our Solar System...

Waves — Basic Principles

Visible light, infrared, ultrasound and so on — they're all <u>waves</u>, and they have certain features in common.

All Waves Have <u>Wavelength, Frequency, Amplitude</u> and <u>Speed</u>

1) <u>WAVELENGTH</u> is the distance from one peak to the next.
2) <u>FREQUENCY</u> is how many <u>complete waves</u> there are <u>per second</u> (passing a certain point). It's measured in <u>hertz</u> (Hz). 1 <u>Hz</u> is 1 wave per second. High frequencies are often given in <u>kHz</u> (1 kHz = 1000 Hz) or <u>MHz</u> (1 MHz = 1 000 000 Hz).
3) <u>AMPLITUDE</u> is just the height of the wave (from the mid-line to the peak).
4) The <u>SPEED</u> is, well, how fast it goes.
5) One <u>important</u> thing to remember is that <u>waves transfer energy and information</u> — <u>without</u> transferring <u>matter</u>.

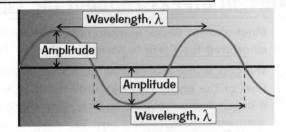

<u>There are</u> Two Formulas <u>for</u> Wave Speed <u>That You</u> Need to Know

1) The first formula links speed, frequency and wavelength:

$$\text{Speed} = \text{Frequency} \times \text{Wavelength}$$
(m/s)   (Hz)   (m)

OR

Speed (v is for <u>velocity</u>)

$$v = f \times \lambda$$

Wavelength (that's the Greek letter 'lambda')

Frequency

<u>EXAMPLE:</u>   Eva is on the beach. She estimates that 2 waves pass her each second, and that the crests of the waves are 12 cm apart. Calculate the speed, in metres per second, of the waves.

<u>ANSWER:</u>   Speed = 2 × 0.12 = 0.24 m/s.

You won't always be asked for the speed though, so you might need this good old triangle too...

2 <u>waves</u> pass <u>per second</u> — so the frequency is <u>2 Hz</u> (hertz)

2) The second formula links wave speed, distance and time:

$$\text{wave speed} = \frac{\text{distance (m)}}{\text{time (s)}}$$
(m/s)

Here's another useful triangle just in case...

Distance

Waves can be <u>Transverse</u> or <u>Longitudinal</u>

<u>Most waves</u> are <u>TRANSVERSE</u>:   1)   <u>Light</u> and <u>all other EM waves</u> (p.76).   3)   <u>Waves</u> on <u>strings</u> and <u>springs</u>.
                                         2)   <u>S-waves</u> (p.92).   4)   <u>Ripples</u> on water.

In <u>TRANSVERSE</u> waves the vibrations are at <u>90°</u> to the <u>DIRECTION OF TRAVEL</u> of the wave.

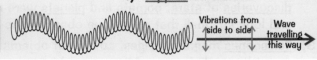

Vibrations from side to side   Wave travelling this way

<u>Some</u> <u>LONGITUDINAL</u> waves are: 1)   <u>Sound</u> and <u>ultrasound</u>.   2) <u>P-waves</u> (p.92).
                                     3)   A <u>slinky spring</u> when you <u>push</u> and <u>pull</u> the end.

In <u>LONGITUDINAL</u> waves the vibrations are along the <u>SAME DIRECTION</u> as the wave is travelling.

One wavelength   Rarefactions   Vibrations in same direction as wave is travelling

Compressions

Oscilloscopes always show things as <u>transverse waves</u> — even <u>sound</u>.

Dude — the waves on this page are like totally rad...

Try this: A sound wave has a frequency of 19 kHz and a wavelength of 12.5 cm. Find its speed.*

Reflection and Refraction

All waves can be <u>reflected</u>. They can also be <u>refracted</u> — it's a fancy way of saying '<u>change direction</u>'.

Waves Can be Reflected

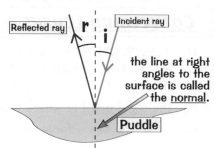

1) When a wave hits a boundary between one medium and another, some of its energy is <u>reflected</u>. This is why you can sometimes see your reflection in puddles — light is reflected back at you.

2) The <u>angle of reflection</u>, r, is the same as the <u>angle of incidence</u>, i.

3) The light's reflected because of the <u>change in density</u> — water is <u>denser</u> than <u>air</u>. Whenever a wave reaches a medium with a different density, <u>some</u> of the wave is <u>reflected at the boundary</u>. This is how ultrasound scanning works (see p.89) — different body tissues have different densities.

Waves Can be Refracted

1) Waves travel at <u>different speeds</u> in substances which have <u>different densities</u>. EM waves travel more <u>slowly</u> in <u>denser</u> media (usually). Sound waves travel faster in <u>denser</u> substances.

2) So when a wave crosses a boundary between two substances, from glass to air, say, it <u>changes speed</u>.

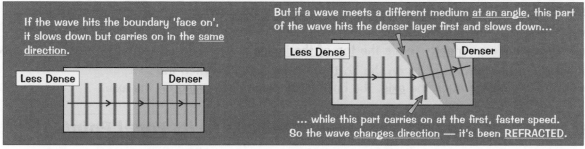

3) When light shines on a glass <u>window pane</u>, some of the light is reflected, but a lot of it passes through the glass and gets <u>refracted</u> as it does so. This is what happens:

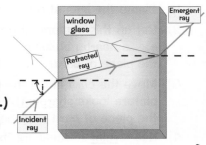

4) As the light passes from the air into the glass (a <u>denser</u> medium), it <u>slows down</u>. This causes the light ray to bend <u>towards</u> the normal.

5) When the light reaches the 'glass to air' boundary on the other side of the window, it's passing into a <u>less dense</u> medium. So it <u>speeds up</u> and bends <u>away</u> from the normal. (Some of the light is also <u>reflected</u> at this boundary.)

6) The light ray that emerges on the other side of the glass is now travelling in the same direction it was to begin with — it's been refracted towards the normal and then back again by the same amount.

7) You can see the 'bending' effect of refraction pretty easily — get something <u>straight</u>, like a pencil, and hold it partly submerged in a fish tank (or if you don't have a fish tank, a glass of water will do).

A Real Image is Actually There — A Virtual Image Is Not

1) A <u>real image</u> is where the <u>light from an object</u> comes together to form an <u>image on a 'screen'</u>.

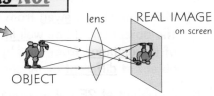

2) A <u>virtual image</u> is when the rays are diverging, so the light from the object <u>appears</u> to be coming from a completely <u>different place</u>.

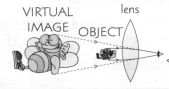

3) When you look in a <u>mirror</u> you see a <u>virtual image</u> of your face — because the <u>object</u> (your face) <u>appears</u> to be <u>behind the mirror</u>.

4) You can get a virtual image when looking at an object through a <u>magnifying lens</u> — the virtual image looks <u>bigger</u> and <u>further away</u> than the object <u>actually</u> is.

Denser media — lead newspapers...

Learn the straightforward rule: <u>more dense</u> materials <u>slow light down</u>, <u>less dense</u> materials <u>speed it up</u>.

Lenses

Lenses are usually made of <u>glass or plastic</u>. All lenses change the <u>direction of light rays</u> by <u>refraction</u> (p.73).

Converging Lenses <u>are Used to</u> Focus Light

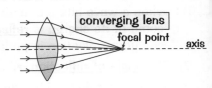

1) A <u>converging</u> lens is <u>convex</u> — it <u>bulges outwards</u>. It causes parallel rays of <u>light</u> to converge (move <u>together</u>) to a <u>focus</u>.
2) The <u>axis</u> of a lens is a line passing through the <u>middle</u> of the lens.
3) The <u>focal point</u> is where rays hitting the lens parallel to the axis all <u>meet</u>.
4) Each lens has a focal point <u>in front</u> of the lens, and one <u>behind</u>.

Draw a <u>Ray Diagram</u> for an <u>Image</u> Through a <u>Converging Lens</u>

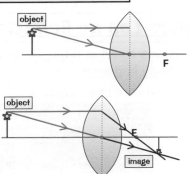

1) Pick a point on the <u>top</u> of the object. Draw a ray going from the object to the lens <u>parallel</u> to the axis of the lens.
2) Draw another ray from the top of the object going right through the middle of the lens.
3) The incident ray that's <u>parallel</u> to the axis is <u>refracted</u> through the <u>focal point</u>. Draw a <u>refracted ray</u> passing through the <u>focal point</u>.
4) The ray passing through the <u>middle</u> of the lens doesn't bend.
5) Mark where the rays <u>meet</u>. That's the <u>top of the image</u>.
6) Repeat the process for a point on the bottom of the object. When the bottom of the object is on the <u>axis</u>, the bottom of the image is <u>also</u> on the axis.

Focal Length <u>is the</u> Distance From <u>the Lens</u> to its Focal Point

A simple <u>experiment</u> can be used to work out the <u>focal length</u> of a converging lens:

1) Clamp the lens at one end of a <u>track</u>. Then clamp a piece of white card <u>further</u> down the track.
2) Set up this equipment near a window with the lens directed at a <u>distant object</u>, e.g. a nearby building — you should be able to see an <u>image</u> of the object on the piece of card. Turn off any lights in the room to make the image more visible.

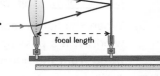

3) Move the card along the track until the image is <u>focused</u> (this is where the picture looks <u>sharpest</u>). When you've got the best image you can — clamp the piece of card in place so it doesn't move.
4) Use a <u>ruler</u> to measure the <u>distance</u> between the <u>centre</u> of the lens and the card — this is the <u>focal length</u>.

Distance <u>from the Lens Affects the</u> Image

You can also do an <u>experiment</u> to find out <u>how</u> an object's distance from the lens affects the image:

1) Use the same apparatus as above — this time put an <u>object</u> on the <u>other</u> side of the lens to the card.
2) Move the object <u>away</u> from the lens and move the card until you get a <u>focused</u> image of the object. The object should be <u>well lit</u>, but the screen shouldn't (to make the image easier to see). Make a note of the <u>distance</u> from the object to the lens, and from the lens to the card. Do this a few times with the object at <u>different</u> distances from the lens. You should find:

a) An object <u>at 2F</u> will produce a <u>real</u>, <u>upside down</u> image the <u>same size</u> as the object, and <u>at 2F</u>.

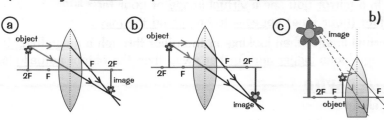

b) <u>Between F and 2F</u> it'll make a <u>real</u>, <u>upside down</u> image <u>bigger</u> than the object, and <u>beyond 2F</u>.

c) An object <u>nearer than F</u> won't appear on the screen, but will make a <u>virtual</u> image the <u>right way up</u>, <u>bigger</u> than the object, on the <u>same side</u> of the lens.

Simple and Reflecting Telescopes

Converging lenses are used in optical telescopes — these are telescopes that collect and focus light. The two types you need to know about are simple refracting and reflecting telescopes.

A Refracting Telescope uses Two Converging Lenses

A refracting telescope is made up of an objective lens and an eyepiece lens.

1) The rays from the object (e.g. a star) are coming from so far away that when they reach the objective lens they're pretty much parallel. The objective lens then converges these rays to form a real image at the focal point of the objective lens.

2) The rays of light from the real image enter the eyepiece lens. The lens spreads them out so they leave at a wider angle than they entered it — and so the light rays fill more of your retina (the 'screen' at the back of your eye) — this makes the image look magnified (bigger).

You don't need to know how to draw this diagram — hoorah.

parallel rays from object in space — objective lens — real image — magnified virtual image at infinity — eyepiece lens

Concave Mirrors are Shiny on the Inside of the Curve

To understand how a reflecting telescope works you first need to know how a concave mirror works — and how a ray diagram of a reflection in one is drawn...

> 1) An incident ray parallel to the axis will pass through the focal point when it's reflected.
> 2) An incident ray passing through the focal point will be parallel to the axis when it's reflected.

1) Pick a point on the top of the object. Draw a ray going from the object to the mirror parallel to the axis of the mirror.

2) Draw another line going from the top of the object to the mirror, passing through the focal point on the way.

3) The incident ray that's parallel to the axis is reflected through the focal point. Draw a reflected ray passing through the focal point.

4) The incident ray that passes through the focal point is reflected parallel to the axis. Draw a reflected ray passing parallel to the axis.

5) Mark where the two reflected rays meet. That's the top of the image.

6) Repeat the process for a point on the bottom of the object. When the bottom of the object is on the axis, the bottom of the image is also on the axis.

I use my telescope to look at the moooon

A Reflecting Telescope uses Mirrors and a Converging Lens

Many reflecting telescopes look like this:

1) A large concave mirror collects the parallel rays of light from an object in space.

2) The larger mirror reflects this light onto a smaller convex mirror placed in front of the large mirror's focal point.

3) The smaller mirror reflects the light through a hole in the centre of the large collecting mirror. A real image is formed behind the mirror.

4) A converging eyepiece lens is used to magnify this image — just like in the refracting telescope.

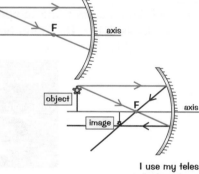

large concave mirror — hole — real image — eye lens — magnified virtual image at infinity — focal point of large concave mirror — second convex mirror

I can't find my telescope — I wonder who I lens it to...

They're quite keen on making sure you know what all this physics is actually used for. In this case, it's the joys of telescopes. Make sure you're happy with how converging lenses work first — then get to grips with this page.

Electromagnetic Waves

You almost certainly use electromagnetic waves every day of your life — so learn to love them.

There are Seven Types of Electromagnetic (EM) Waves

The EM spectrum is split into seven groups — these are shown below with their wavelengths.
The groups shown actually merge into each other — forming a continuous spectrum.

	RADIO WAVES	MICRO WAVES	INFRA RED	VISIBLE LIGHT	ULTRA VIOLET	X-RAYS	GAMMA RAYS
wavelength	$1\ m - 10^4\ m$	$10^{-2}\ m\ (1\ cm)$	$10^{-5}m\ (0.01\ mm)$	$10^{-7}\ m$	$10^{-8}\ m$	$10^{-10}\ m$	$10^{-12}\ m$

INCREASING FREQUENCY AND DECREASING WAVELENGTH →

1) All EM waves are transverse waves (see page 72).

2) All the different types of EM wave travel at the same speed (3×10^8 m/s) in a vacuum, e.g. in space.

3) This means EM waves with higher frequencies, like X-rays and γ-rays (gamma rays), have shorter wavelengths

Infrared Radiation was Discovered by Herschel in 1800

Up until the discovery of infrared radiation, visible light was the only part of the EM spectrum
that scientists knew existed. Herschel found infrared when experimenting with sunlight and a prism:

1) When white light goes through a prism, it creates a spectrum of colours (see diagram below).
Herschel used this equipment to create a spectrum on a screen.

2) He wanted to know about the amount of heat in each of these colours — he used a thermometer to
measure each colour's temperature in turn. He noticed they increased from violet to red.

3) He then measured the temperature just past the red part of the spectrum where there was
no visible light. He found here had the highest temperature of all — he had discovered infrared,
an invisible type of radiation.

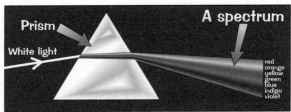

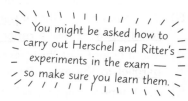

You might be asked how to
carry out Herschel and Ritter's
experiments in the exam —
so make sure you learn them.

Ritter Discovered Ultraviolet Radiation Soon After in 1801

A scientist called Ritter began to carry out experiments to see if he could find anything on the other side
of the spectrum beyond violet.

1) Ritter knew silver chloride turned from white to black when exposed to light. So he decided to
measure how quickly silver chloride coated strips changed when exposed to different colours of light.

2) In a dark room, he created a spectrum using a light source and a prism and exposed the strips of
paper to each colour. He timed how long it took the strips to turn black.

3) The strips changed quickest when exposed to light nearer the blue end of the spectrum.

4) He then placed a strip in the area just past the violet part of the spectrum — here
he saw the quickest change of all. Ritter had discovered ultraviolet radiation,
an invisible form of light that exists on the other side of the visible spectrum.

Herschel and Ritter — not to be confused with Hansel and Gretel...

Herschel and Ritter's work was really important to physics — it showed that other types of waves beyond the
visible spectrum existed. Over the next 100 years or so the other types of EM waves (shown in the diagram at
the top) were also discovered. One massively important thing to remember about EM waves is that they all travel
at the same speed in a vacuum (e.g. space) — those pesky examiners might try to catch you out on that.

The Dangers of Electromagnetic Radiation

You can't escape EM radiation — it's very useful in many ways, but it can be <u>dangerous</u> too.

The <u>Properties</u> of EM Waves <u>Depend on Their</u> <u>Frequency</u>

1) As the <u>frequency</u> of EM radiation changes, its <u>interaction with matter</u> changes — i.e. the way a wave is <u>absorbed</u>, <u>reflected</u> or <u>transmitted</u> by any given substance <u>depends entirely</u> on its <u>frequency</u>.

2) As a rule, the EM waves at <u>each end</u> of the spectrum tend to be able to <u>pass through material</u>, whilst those <u>nearer the middle</u> are <u>absorbed</u>.

3) The <u>effects</u> of <u>EM radiation</u> on humans depends on the <u>frequency</u> of the EM waves, since frequency determines the <u>energy of the waves</u>.

4) Generally, the higher the frequency, the <u>more energy</u> the radiation has, and so the <u>more harmful</u> the radiation.

5) Make sure you know how <u>exposure</u> to each <u>type</u> of <u>radiation</u> in the table below <u>affects human tissue</u>.

<u>Some</u> EM Radiation <u>Can be</u> <u>Harmful</u> <u>to People</u>

INCREASING FREQUENCY

<u>MICRO-WAVES</u>	<u>Microwaves</u> have a <u>similar frequency</u> to the <u>vibrations</u> of many <u>molecules</u>, and so increase these vibrations — resulting in <u>heating</u> (as in <u>microwave ovens</u>). Microwaves can HEAT HUMAN BODY CELLS this way. <u>Mobile phones</u> use <u>microwaves</u>, and their increasing use has caused <u>concern</u>, as the handset is often <u>held close</u> to the <u>brain</u>. There have been <u>suggested</u> links with <u>brain tumours</u>, but <u>nothing</u> has been <u>proved</u>.
<u>INFRA-RED</u>	The <u>infrared</u> range of frequencies can make the <u>surface molecules</u> of any substance <u>vibrate</u> — and like microwaves, this has a <u>heating effect</u>. But infrared has a <u>higher frequency</u>, so carries <u>more energy</u> than microwave radiation. If the <u>human body</u> is exposed to <u>too much infrared</u> radiation, it can cause some nasty <u>SKIN BURNS</u>.
<u>ULTRA-VIOLET</u>	UV radiation has got <u>more energy</u> and a <u>higher</u> frequency than infrared radiation. It's '<u>ionising</u>' — it carries <u>enough energy</u> to knock electrons off atoms. <u>SUNBURN</u> happens when surface skin cells have been damaged by absorbing UV rays in sunlight. This can cause <u>cell mutation or destruction</u>, and <u>SKIN CANCER</u>. The <u>UV</u> in <u>sunlight</u> can also cause <u>EYE DAMAGE</u>. 
<u>GAMMA/ X-RAYS</u>	<u>Very high-frequency</u> waves, such as <u>gamma rays</u> and <u>X-rays</u>, are also <u>ionising</u>, and carry <u>much more energy</u> than UV rays. This means they can be <u>much more damaging</u> and they can <u>penetrate further</u> into the body. Like all ionising radiation, they can cause <u>CELL MUTATION</u> or <u>destruction</u>, leading to <u>tissue damage</u> or <u>CANCER</u> (see page 81).

When it comes to how harmful an EM wave is — size really does matter...

The various types of EM radiation all have different properties because they all have <u>different frequencies</u>. Remember that the higher the frequency, the <u>more dangerous</u> an EM wave potentially is. It's not all doom and gloom though — even EM waves with high frequencies (e.g. gamma rays) have really important uses.

Radio Waves and Microwaves

You use EM waves (see p.76) for <u>all sorts of stuff</u> — your <u>satellite TV</u> (and your <u>terrestrial TV</u>), your <u>radio</u>, your <u>microwave oven</u>, your <u>pet dog Jimbo</u>... OK maybe not that last bit.

Radio Waves are Used Mainly for Communications

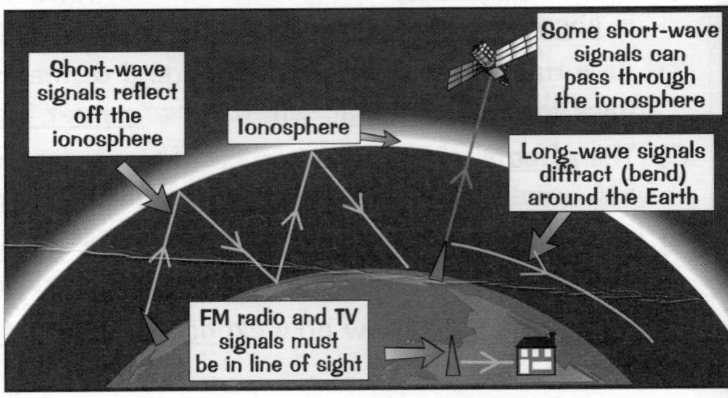

1) <u>Radio waves</u> are used to broadcast <u>TV and radio</u> signals and to <u>transmit satellite</u> signals (in the same way as <u>microwaves</u> — see below).

2) <u>Long-wave radio</u> (wavelengths of <u>1 – 10 km</u>) can be transmitted from London, say, and received halfway round the world. That's because long wavelengths <u>bend</u> around the curved surface of the Earth. They also get around <u>hills</u>, into <u>tunnels</u> and all sorts.

3) The radio waves used for <u>TV and FM radio</u> transmissions have very short wavelengths (10 cm – 10 m). To get reception, you must be in <u>direct sight of the transmitter</u> — the signal doesn't bend around hills or travel far <u>through</u> buildings.

4) <u>Short-wave radio</u> signals (wavelengths of about <u>10 m – 100 m</u>) can, like long-wave, be received at <u>long distances</u> from the transmitter. That's because they are <u>reflected</u> from the <u>ionosphere</u> — an <u>electrically charged layer</u> in the Earth's upper atmosphere. <u>Medium-wave</u> signals (well, the shorter ones) can also reflect from the ionosphere, depending on atmospheric conditions and time of day.

5) Some <u>very short-wave</u> radio waves can <u>pass</u> through the ionosphere — so they can be used for <u>satellite communications</u> (see below).

Diagram labels:
Short-wave signals reflect off the ionosphere
Ionosphere
Some short-wave signals can pass through the ionosphere
Long-wave signals diffract (bend) around the Earth
FM radio and TV signals must be in line of sight

Microwaves are Used for Satellite Communication and Mobile Phones

1) Communication to and from <u>satellites</u> (including satellite TV signals and satellite phones) uses microwaves. But you need to use microwaves which can <u>pass easily</u> through the Earth's <u>watery atmosphere</u>.

2) For satellite TV, the signal from a <u>transmitter</u> is transmitted into space...

3) ... where it's picked up by the satellite receiver dish <u>orbiting</u> thousands of kilometres above the Earth. The satellite <u>transmits</u> the signal back to Earth in a different direction...

microwaves
clouds and water vapour

4) ... where it's received by a <u>satellite dish</u> on the ground. There is a slight <u>time delay</u> between the signal being sent and <u>received</u>, e.g. from the UK to Australia, because of the <u>long distance</u> the signal has to travel.

5) Mobile phone signals also travel from your phone to the nearest <u>transmitter</u> as <u>microwaves</u>.

Microwave Ovens Use a Different Microwave Wavelength from Satellites

1) In <u>communications</u>, the microwaves used need to <u>pass through</u> the Earth's watery atmosphere.

2) In <u>microwave ovens</u>, the microwaves need to be <u>absorbed</u> by <u>water molecules</u> in food to be able to heat it up — so they use a <u>different</u> wavelength to those used in satellite communications.

3) The microwaves penetrate up to a few centimetres into the food before being <u>absorbed</u> by water molecules. The energy from the absorbed microwaves causes the food to heat up. The heat energy is then <u>conducted</u> or <u>convected</u> to other parts of the food.

Revision time — adjust depending on brain wattage...

If you're asked for uses of microwaves, then microwave ovens will probably be the first answer you think of. But don't forget they're used in <u>communications</u> too — it's just a different wavelength of microwave that's used.

Infrared Radiation

If you were thinking of turning to a life of crime, beware — waves are out to get you...

Infrared Radiation Can be Used to Monitor Temperature

1) Infrared radiation (or IR) is also known as heat radiation. It's given out by all hot objects — and the hotter the object, the more IR radiation it gives out.

2) This means infrared can be used to monitor temperatures. For example, heat loss through a house's uninsulated roof can be detected using infrared sensors.

3) Infrared is also detected by night-vision equipment. The equipment turns it into an electrical signal, which is displayed on a screen as a picture. The hotter an object is, the brighter it appears. Police and the military use this to spot baddies running away, like you've seen on TV.

Optical Fibres Use Infrared to Transmit Data

1) Optical fibres can carry data over long distances as pulses of infrared (IR) radiation, e.g. in telephone cables.

2) They work by bouncing waves off the sides of a thin inner core of glass or plastic. The wave enters one end of the fibre and is reflected repeatedly until it emerges at the other end.

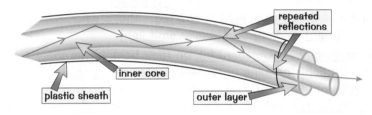

Infrared Has Many Other Uses Around the Home...

Infrared radiation can be used in cooking, e.g. in grills and toasters.

Remote controls transfer information to TVs and DVD players using infrared radiation.

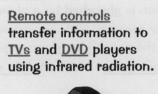

Infrared can be used to transmit information between mobile phones or computers — but only over short distances.

Infrared sensors are used in security systems, e.g. burglar alarms and security lights. These sensors detect heat from an intruder's body.

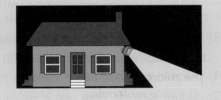

Security lights — great for detecting next door's cat...

Optical fibres are a good way to send data over long distances — the EM waves travel fast, and they can't easily be tapped into or suffer interference (unlike a signal that's broadcast from a transmitter, like radio). The signals do need occasional boosting — some of the IR radiation gets lost because of imperfections in the fibre.

Visible Light, UV and X-rays

You might already know about some of these uses of light, UV and X-rays. But you need to know it all...

We Need Visible Light to See

It might seem pretty obvious, but we only see objects because they're <u>illuminated</u> — they either <u>give out</u> or <u>reflect</u> light. For you to see an object, light needs to <u>enter</u> your eyes. Duh.

1) When light enters your eye, it gets <u>refracted</u> (see page 73) through the lens and <u>focused</u> onto the retina at the back of the eye. The retina then sends <u>messages</u> to the brain (via the optic nerve), and the <u>very clever</u> brain <u>interprets</u> them. Ta da — you can see.

2) Photography works in a <u>similar</u> way to the eye. Cameras use a <u>lens</u> to focus <u>visible light</u> onto a light-sensitive <u>film</u> or electronic <u>sensor</u> that <u>records</u> the image.

3) The lens's <u>aperture</u> controls <u>how much</u> light enters the camera.

4) The <u>shutter speed</u> determines the <u>how long</u> the film or sensor is <u>exposed</u> to the light.

5) By varying the <u>aperture</u> and <u>shutter speed</u>, a photographer can capture as much or as little light as they want in their photograph.

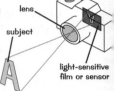

lens
subject
light-sensitive film or sensor

Ultraviolet Radiation is Used to Detect Forged Bank Notes

1) <u>Fluorescence</u> is a property of certain chemicals, where <u>ultraviolet radiation (UV)</u> is <u>absorbed</u> and then <u>visible light</u> is <u>emitted</u>. That's why fluorescent colours look so <u>bright</u> — they do actually <u>emit light</u>.

2) <u>Banks</u> now print <u>special markings</u> in <u>fluorescent ink</u> on their <u>bank notes</u> to detect <u>forgeries</u>. <u>Under a UV light</u>, <u>genuine</u> notes will <u>display</u> the special <u>fluorescent markings</u>... <u>Fake</u> notes, on the other hand, are often printed on <u>cheaper paper</u> that's <u>slightly fluorescent</u>, so under UV, they'll <u>glow all over</u>, and there'll be <u>no markings</u>.

3) Here, it's the amount of radiation <u>emitted</u> that you're detecting and measuring.

4) <u>Fluorescent lamps</u> (like the ones you might have in your <u>classroom</u>) use UV radiation to <u>emit</u> visible light. They're <u>safe</u> to use as <u>all</u> the UV radiation is <u>absorbed</u> by a phosphor coating on the inside of the glass.

5) <u>Security pens</u> can be used to <u>mark</u> your property with your name (e.g. laptops). The ink in the pen is only visible in <u>UV light</u> — this can help the police <u>identify</u> your property if it's stolen.

6) UV radiation can also be used to <u>disinfect water</u> — the UV <u>kills off</u> any viruses and bacteria in the water, making it <u>safer</u> to use.

To the naked eye:
10 10 / 10 10 10
genuine   fake

Under UV light:
10 10 /
10
genuine   fake

X-Rays are Used to Look Inside Objects

1) <u>Radiographers</u> in <u>hospitals</u> take <u>X-ray 'photographs'</u> of people to see if they have any <u>broken bones</u>.

2) X-rays pass <u>easily through flesh</u> but not so easily through <u>denser material</u> like <u>bones</u> or <u>metal</u>. So it's the amount of radiation that's <u>absorbed</u> (or <u>not absorbed</u>) that gives you an X-ray image.

3) X-rays can cause <u>cancer</u>, so radiographers wear <u>lead aprons</u> and stand behind a <u>lead screen</u> or <u>leave the room</u> to keep their <u>exposure</u> to X-rays to a <u>minimum</u>.

4) Airport security use X-rays to scan <u>luggage</u> to check for suspicious-looking objects.

5) Some airports now use X-ray scanners on <u>passengers</u> to look for concealed weapons or explosives — low-level X-rays are used so they <u>aren't</u> as harmful as the X-rays used in <u>hospitals</u>.

The <u>brighter bits</u> are where <u>fewer X-rays</u> get through. This is a <u>negative image</u>. The plate starts off <u>all white</u>.

Don't lie to an X-ray — they can see right through you...

Pretty interesting stuff, this, I reckon. All the waves on this page are types of EM waves. You don't need to understand all the ins and outs of EM waves for this little bit — it's more the idea of how they can be used.

Gamma Rays and Ionising Radiation

Gamma rays may be one cause of cancer — but they also have some important uses...

Radiotherapy — the Treatment of Cancer Using γ-Rays

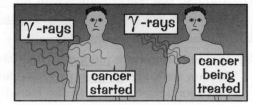

1) Since high doses of gamma rays will kill all living cells, they can be used to treat cancers.

2) The gamma rays have to be directed carefully and at just the right dosage so as to kill the cancer cells without killing too many normal cells.

3) However, a fair bit of damage is inevitably done to normal cells, which makes the patient feel very ill. But if the cancer is successfully killed off in the end, then it's worth it.

4) Gamma rays can also be used to diagnose cancer. A radioactive isotope is injected into the patient — a gamma camera is then used to detect where the radioactive isotope travels in the body. This creates an image which can then be used to detect where there might be cancer.

Sterilisation of Food and Surgical Instruments Uses γ-Rays

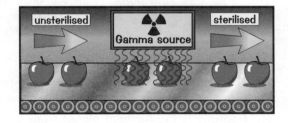

1) Food can be exposed to a high dose of gamma rays which will kill all microbes, keeping the food fresh for longer.

2) Medical instruments can be sterilised in just the same way, rather than by boiling them.

3) The great advantage of irradiation over boiling is that it doesn't involve high temperatures, so things like fresh apples or plastic instruments can be totally sterilised without damaging them.

4) The food is not radioactive afterwards, so it's perfectly safe to eat.

5) The radioactive isotope used for this needs to be a very strong emitter of gamma rays.

Gamma Radiation is One of the Three Types of Ionising Radiation

The other two types of ionising radiation are alpha (α) and beta (β).

1) Ionising radiation is emitted all the time by radioactive sources when their nuclei decay.

2) This emission is completely random and so you can't predict when it'll happen for a given nucleus — but when it does, it'll spit out one or more of the three types of ionising radiation (alpha, beta and gamma).

3) All three types transfer energy — that's why they're called ionising radiation. They're so energetic that they bash into atoms and knock electrons off them.

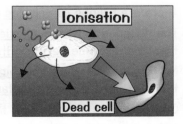

4) Alpha, beta and gamma all have their own uses — but they can also be very dangerous. For example, if radiation enters your body it will collide with molecules in your cells. These collisions cause ionisation, which damages or destroys the molecules — which can lead to cancer.

Learn your alphabet-agamma...

It's quite difficult to do research on how radiation affects humans. This is partly because it would be very unethical to do controlled experiments, exposing people to huge doses of radiation just to see what happens. We rely mostly on studies of populations affected by nuclear accidents or nuclear bombs.

The Solar System

Our Solar System is made up of the Sun, <u>orbited</u> by the planets Mercury, Venus, Earth, Mars, Jupiter, Saturn, Uranus and Neptune. Oh, and an asteroid belt chucked in for good measure between Mars and Jupiter.

Planets <u>Reflect Sunlight</u> and Orbit the <u>Sun</u> in <u>Ellipses</u>

1) You can <u>see</u> some planets with the <u>naked eye</u>. They look like <u>stars</u>, but they're <u>totally different</u>.

2) All planets orbit around <u>stars</u>.

3) Planets often have <u>moons</u> orbiting around them. Moons are usually <u>much smaller</u> than their planets, and found pretty <u>close</u> to the planet.

Our Solar System

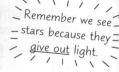
Remember we see stars because they <u>give out</u> light.

4) In the diagram below, the sizes of the Moon, Earth and Sun are to scale. But there's only room on the page to show about 1° of the Sun's circumference — it's <u>so</u> enormous compared to the planets.

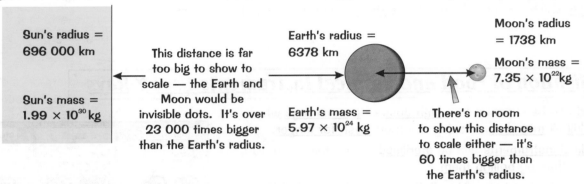

Sun's radius = 696 000 km

Sun's mass = 1.99×10^{30} kg

This distance is far too big to show to scale — the Earth and Moon would be invisible dots. It's over 23 000 times bigger than the Earth's radius.

Earth's radius = 6378 km

Earth's mass = 5.97×10^{24} kg

Moon's radius = 1738 km

Moon's mass = 7.35×10^{22} kg

There's no room to show this distance to scale either — it's 60 times bigger than the Earth's radius.

5) The planets in our Solar System vary <u>massively</u> in size. <u>Mercury</u>, the smallest planet, has a radius <u>285 times</u> smaller than the Sun's. Even the biggest planet, Jupiter, has a radius <u>10 times</u> smaller than the Sun's.

6) Neptune is the <u>furthest</u> planet from the Sun — it's about <u>30 times</u> further from the Sun than the Earth is.

7) <u>Manned spacecraft</u> can reach the moon in <u>3 days</u> and one <u>could</u> potentially reach Mars in around <u>9 months</u>. A manned spacecraft to <u>Neptune</u> would take <u>at least</u> 12 years — and that's only <u>one-way</u>. Eek.

Our <u>Sun</u> <u>is in</u> the <u>Milky Way Galaxy</u>

1) A <u>galaxy</u> is a collection of <u>billions</u> of stars. The <u>Sun</u> is one of <u>many billions</u> of <u>stars</u> which form the <u>Milky Way galaxy</u>.

2) The <u>distance</u> between neighbouring stars is often <u>hundreds of thousands of times greater</u> than the distance between <u>planets</u> in our Solar System. After the Sun, the <u>nearest</u> star to us is 4×10^{13} km away.

3) There are <u>billions</u> of <u>galaxies</u> which all make up the <u>universe</u>.

4) The <u>distance</u> between <u>galaxies</u> is often <u>millions of times greater</u> than the distance <u>between the stars</u> inside a galaxy.

5) No one is really sure <u>how big</u> the universe is. We do know that the light from the <u>most distant</u> galaxies (that we can see) takes <u>billions</u> of years to reach us.

6) Compare that with the fact that light takes about <u>500 seconds</u> to reach us on <u>Earth</u> from the <u>Sun</u> — and you'll maybe get a bit more of an idea how <u>ENORMOUS</u> the universe really is.

You are here

For really big distances like this, astronomers sometimes use the units of light years. 1 light year (ly) is the distance that light would travel through a vacuum in one year. 1 ly = 9.5×10^{12} km

Revision's hard work — you've got to plan et...

Scientists have always argued about what makes a planet a planet, but they finally decided in 2006. So, is <u>Pluto</u> a planet? It's much smaller than the others, has a different orbit, and a moon almost as big as itself. And what about this 10th 'planet' discovered recently (<u>2003 UB</u>$_{313}$, or '<u>Eris</u>' to its mates), which is bigger than Pluto, but has an even weirder orbit? <u>No</u> and <u>no</u>... apparently. So there you go.

Is Anybody Out There?

If you want to find out about whether there is life beyond Earth, you could get in a spaceship and go out into the universe to see — but that's pretty difficult, expensive and dangerous. There are easier ways...

Some Scientists are Looking for Signs of Life

1) Many scientists want to try and find out if there's life out there. Space exploration is very expensive, and impractical for anything beyond the Solar System — the distances are just too large. Scientists usually use Earth-based telescopes or other remote-sensing techniques (see p.84) to get some initial clues — before they spend loads of money sending robots or people for a closer look.

2) Scientists haven't found anything exciting, but they are using these methods to search for planets with suitable conditions for life.

SETI Looks for Radio Signals from Other Planets

1) Us Earthlings are constantly beaming radio, TV and radar into space for any passing aliens to detect. There might be life out there that's as clever as we are. Or even more clever. They may have built transmitters to send out signals like ours.

2) SETI stands for Search for ExtraTerrestrial Intelligence. Scientists on the SETI project are looking for narrow bands of radio wavelengths (see p.76) coming to Earth from outer space. They're looking for meaningful signals in all the 'noise'.

3) Signals in a narrow band could have come from a transmitter. The 'noise' comes from other things like giant stars.

4) It takes ages to analyse all the radio waves, so the SETI folk get help from the public — you can download a screensaver off the Internet which analyses a chunk of radio waves.

5) SETI has been going for about 50 years but they've not found anything. Not a sausage. ☹

6) Scientists are now looking for possible laser signals from outer space. Watch this space...

Robots and Probes Can Collect Data and Samples

Scientists sometimes send spacecraft to try and collect evidence of life.

1) Spacecraft carrying probes have been sent to investigate planets and moons in our Solar System, such as Mars and Titan (one of Saturn's moons). These probes carry instruments which can continuously record data about conditions, e.g. temperature. All this data is sent back to Earth on microwave or radio signals.

2) Robots, like the 1976 Mars Viking landers, can take photos and collect soil and rock samples to analyse. The landers took soil samples using a robotic arm and carried out experiments on the soil to see if they could find any signs of life, e.g. bacteria — the results were sent to Earth using radio signals.

3) Robots don't do all the hard work though. Scientists still have to work out what the data means — for instance, this photograph from a meteorite from Mars could be evidence that life exists (or has existed) on Mars, but it could be lots of other things.

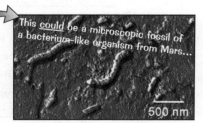

This could be a microscopic fossil of a bacterium-like organism from Mars...

Then again, it could be a crystal, some bits of metal or the remains of last night's curry...

4) Scientists don't just look for life on other planets — they look at comets and asteroids too. In 2003, the Hayabusa Spacecraft was sent to collect a sample of dust from a nearby asteroid. This was the first ever attempt to send a spacecraft that would collect an asteroid sample and then bring it back to Earth for analysis.

Intelligent life — don't flatter yourself...

Science fiction aside, we haven't really found that much yet. But you can see why they keep trying — it's such a tantalising thought. Other beings on another planet at the other side of the universe... Would they be trying to discover US? If we found each other, could we communicate? Blows my mind.

Looking into Space

There are various objects in space, and they emit or reflect different frequencies of EM radiation.
And that can be really useful to help us find out what's going on 'out there'.

Space Telescopes Have a Clearer View Than Those on Earth

Telescopes help you to see distant objects clearly. But there can be problems...

1) If you're trying to detect light, Earth's atmosphere gets in the way — it absorbs a lot of the light coming from space before it can reach us. To observe the frequencies absorbed, you have to go above the atmosphere.

2) Then there's pollution. Light pollution (light thrown up into the sky from street lamps, etc.) makes it hard to pick out dim objects. And air pollution (e.g. dust particles) can reflect and absorb light coming from space. So to get the best view possible from Earth, a telescope should be on top of a mountain (where there's less atmosphere above it), and far away from any cities (e.g. on Hawaii).

Night sky in rural area with no light pollution.   Night sky in urban area with light pollution.

3) But to avoid the problem of the atmosphere, the thing to do is put your telescope in space, away from the mist and murk down here. The first space telescope (called Hubble) was launched by NASA in 1990. It can see objects that are about a billion times fainter than you can see unaided from Earth.

Different Telescopes Detect Different Types of EM Wave

To get as full a picture of the universe as possible, you need to detect different kinds of EM wave (p.76).

1) The earliest telescopes were all optical telescopes which detect visible light. They're used to look at objects close by and in other galaxies. But many objects in the universe aren't detectable using visible light — so other types of EM telescopes are needed to observe them.

2) From the 1940s onwards, telescopes were developed for all parts of the EM spectrum. These modern telescopes mean we can now 'see' parts of the universe that we couldn't see before and learn more about the universe, e.g. its structure.

3) Cygnus A is a nearby galaxy. When you look at it through an optical telescope, you see the galaxy as a small blob, surrounded by stars. When observed using a radio telescope instead, you see two 'radio jets' moving away from the centre of the galaxy in opposite directions — these create two massive 'lobes' of hot radiation. Impressive stuff.

An image of Cygnus A using an optical telescope.   An image of Cygnus A using a radio telescope.

4) X-ray telescopes are a good way to 'see' violent, high-temperature events in space, like exploding stars.

5) Radio telescopes were responsible for the discovery of the cosmic microwave background radiation (p.87) — this helped scientists to learn more about the origins of the universe.

6) Telescopes are improving all the time — bigger telescopes give us better resolution (i.e. a lot of detail) and can gather more light, so we can see things we couldn't before as they were too faint. Improved magnification means we can now look further into space — more and more galaxies are being discovered.

7) Discovering more galaxies is important to help scientists learn more about their life cycle. Some pictures taken by the Hubble Space Telescope show galaxies at all different stages of their life. These images are used to help scientists learn more about how galaxies are formed and how they evolve.

8) Modern telescopes often work alongside computers. Computers help create clearer and sharper images and make it easy to capture these pictures so they can be analysed later.

9) Computers make it possible to collect and store huge amounts of data, 24 hours a day, without having to rely on humans. They also make it easier and quicker to analyse all this data.

Telescope broken — we can't get the van up there, mate...

Most telescopes contain a lot of delicate, easily damaged parts. This is why it's so expensive to put them in space (as well as the cost of launching the rocket) — they've got to be strong enough to withstand all the shaking on board the vehicle which takes them into orbit, but they need to be lightweight too. It's hard work being a boffin.

Space and Spectrometry

It's alright learning about all this <u>space stuff</u> — but it's important to get a bit of <u>real-life</u> practice to help you understand it all too. Luckily this page ticks <u>both</u> those boxes — the good times are a-comin'.

Most Large Optical Telescopes Have Spectrometers

A spectrometer is a tool used to <u>analyse</u> the <u>light</u> given out by stars and galaxies.

1) Very simply, it works by the telescope directing a beam of light into the spectrometer and through a <u>slit</u>. This <u>diffracts</u> the light and <u>splits</u> it up into a <u>spectrum</u> — similar to a <u>prism</u> (p.76).

2) The light spectra from stars and galaxies contain <u>dark lines</u> (see picture).

3) These dark lines are caused by the light at those wavelengths being <u>absorbed</u>, e.g. by elements in the star's atmosphere. These patterns of dark lines are called <u>absorption spectra</u>.

4) Absorption spectra can be used to work out what the stars and galaxies are <u>made of</u> — each element has its <u>own</u> particular absorption spectrum.

5) For example, the <u>absorption</u> spectrum you'd see when looking at light from our <u>Sun</u> is <u>very similar to</u> the one you'd see when looking at light from a <u>hydrogen lamp</u>. Which makes sense as the Sun is mostly made of <u>hydrogen</u>.

6) Some spectra have <u>bright lines</u> — these are <u>emission spectra</u>. The lines are caused by extra light being <u>emitted</u> at those wavelengths. Emission spectra can also be used to work out what something is <u>made of</u>.

7) The spectra for galaxies further away appear <u>more red</u> than they should (see page 87).

An example of an absorption spectrum

dark lines

You Can Make a Simple Spectrometer Using a CD

You can <u>analyse</u> the spectra of some common everyday light sources by making a spectrometer. You just need a cardboard box, a CD (or DVD) and some scissors:

1) Make a slit about <u>1 mm</u> wide on one end of the box — this is where the <u>light</u> will come through.

2) Then make a slit for the CD at a <u>45° angle</u> on the side of the box shown in the diagram.

3) Now make a hole to look through (see diagram) by cutting a <u>slot</u> about 2 cm by 6 cm.

4) Put the CD into the box so that the underside of the CD (the "rainbow" side) is <u>facing</u> where you'll look through.

5) Then hold up the box so that it lets in <u>light</u> from your <u>source</u> through the slit — you should be able to see the <u>visible spectrum</u>. (Make sure you do this in a <u>darkened room</u> — so the <u>only</u> light getting into the box is that from your <u>source</u>.)

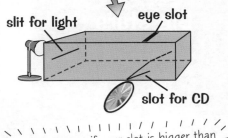

slit for light — eye slot — slot for CD

Watch out — if your slot is bigger than 1 mm your spectrum will be blurry and if it's too small it won't be very bright.

6) Experimenting with different sources of light will show <u>different</u> looking spectra. <u>Ordinary light bulbs</u>, <u>sodium lamps</u> and a <u>white page</u> on a computer screen are good ones to try out.

7) What you'll see using your spectrometer <u>won't</u> look exactly the same as the picture of the <u>absorption spectrum</u> at the top of the page. That's because this is a pretty <u>basic</u> spectrometer. Here are a few pictures to show you the sort of thing you <u>might</u> be able to see:

ordinary light bulb

sodium lamp (e.g. a street lamp)

white page on a laptop screen

This is a <u>continuous spectrum</u> — <u>no light</u> has been <u>absorbed</u> so there are no dark lines.

The <u>bright lines</u> show the wavelengths of light <u>emitted</u>, the <u>dark lines</u> show the wavelengths that <u>weren't</u> emitted.

Looking at light from stars and galaxies — it's a spectra-cle

Spectrometry is a clever thing. It's quite a simple idea, but it's made a <u>huge impact</u> on our understanding of the universe. In fact, most of what we know about what <u>makes up</u> our <u>solar system</u> is because of spectrometry. And to think, you now have the skills to spectrometry away in the comfort of your own home. Splendid. And if you're <u>really</u> interested, look up 'line spectra' on the Internet — you'll see lots more <u>pretty</u> pics of spectra.

The Life Cycle of Stars

Stars go through <u>many traumatic stages</u> in their lives — just like teenagers.

Nebula

1) Stars <u>initially form</u> from <u>clouds of dust and gas</u> called <u>NEBULAS</u>.

2) The <u>force of gravity</u> makes the gas and dust <u>spiral in together</u>. <u>Gravitational energy</u> is converted into <u>heat energy</u>, so the <u>temperature rises</u>.

Main Sequence Star

3) When the <u>temperature</u> gets <u>high enough</u>, <u>hydrogen nuclei</u> undergo <u>thermonuclear fusion</u> to form <u>helium nuclei</u> and give out massive amounts of <u>energy</u>. A star is born. It immediately enters a <u>long stable period</u> where the <u>heat created</u> by the nuclear fusion provides an <u>outward pressure</u> to <u>balance</u> the <u>force of gravity</u> pulling everything <u>inwards</u>. In this stable period it's called a <u>MAIN SEQUENCE STAR</u> and it can last for <u>several billion years</u>. (The Sun is in the middle of this stable period — or to put it another way, the <u>Earth</u> has already had <u>half its innings</u> before the Sun <u>engulfs</u> it.)

4) Eventually the <u>hydrogen</u> in the core begins to <u>run out</u> and the star then <u>swells</u> into a <u>RED GIANT</u> (it becomes <u>red</u> because the surface <u>cools</u>).

Red Giant

Small stars

5) A small-to-medium-sized star like the Sun then becomes unstable and <u>ejects</u> its <u>outer layer</u> of <u>dust and gas</u> as a <u>planetary nebula</u>.

planetary nebula.... and a White Dwarf

6) This leaves behind a <u>hot</u>, <u>dense</u> solid core — a <u>WHITE DWARF</u>, which just <u>cools down</u> and eventually <u>disappears</u>. (That's going to be really sad.)

Big stars

Supernova

7) <u>Big stars</u>, however, start to <u>glow brightly again</u> as they undergo more <u>fusion</u> and <u>expand and contract several times</u>, forming <u>heavier elements</u> in various <u>nuclear reactions</u>. Eventually they'll <u>explode</u> in a <u>SUPERNOVA</u>.

Neutron Star...

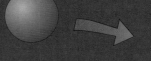

...or Black Hole

8) The <u>exploding supernova</u> throws the outer layers of <u>dust and gas</u> into space, leaving a <u>very dense core</u> called a <u>NEUTRON STAR</u>. If the star is <u>big enough</u> this will become a <u>BLACK HOLE</u>.

Red Giants, White Dwarfs, Black Holes, Green Ghosts...

Erm. Now how do they know that exactly... Anyway, now you know what the future holds — our Sun is going to fizzle out, and it'll just get <u>very very cold</u> and <u>very very dark</u>. Great. On a brighter note, the Sun's got a good few years in it yet, so it's still worth passing those exams.

The Origins of the Universe

Once upon a time, there was a really Big Bang — that's the most convincing theory we've got.

Light from Other Galaxies is Red-Shifted

1) When we look at light from distant galaxies we find that the frequencies are all lower than they should be — they're shifted towards the red end of the spectrum.

2) This is called the red-shift. It's the same effect as the 'vrrr-oomm' from a racing car — the engine noise sounds lower-pitched when the car's gone past you and is moving away from you.

① The sound waves from a stationary car are equally spaced, like this

② But for a moving car, the wavelengths seem longer here...

...than here

③ So the frequency of the sound waves seems to be lower if the car is moving away from you.

3) Measurements of red-shift suggest that all the galaxies are moving away from us very quickly — and it's the same result whichever direction you look in.

4) More distant galaxies have greater red-shifts than nearer ones.

5) This means that more distant galaxies are moving away faster than nearer ones.

6) Red-shift provides evidence that the whole universe is expanding.

There's a Uniform Microwave Radiation from All Directions

1) Scientists have detected low frequency electromagnetic radiation (see p.76) coming from all parts of the universe.

2) This radiation is mainly in the microwave part of the EM spectrum. It's known as the cosmic microwave background radiation (CMB radiation).

3) For complicated reasons, CMB radiation is strong evidence for an initial Big Bang, and as the universe expands and cools, this background radiation 'cools' and drops in frequency.

4) The Big Bang is currently the only theory that provides any explanation for CMB radiation. The discovery of the CMB radiation led to the Big Bang theory being the currently accepted model.

It All Started Off with a Very Big Bang (Probably)

Right now, all the galaxies are moving away from each other at great speed. But something must have got them going. That 'something' was probably a big explosion — so they called it the Big Bang...

1) According to this theory, all the matter and energy in the universe must have been compressed into a very small space. Then it exploded and started expanding.

2) The expansion is still going on. We can use the current rate of expansion of the universe to estimate its age. Our best guess is that the Big Bang happened about 14 billion years ago.

3) These estimates might not be very accurate, partly because it's hard to tell how much the expansion has slowed down since the Big Bang.

4) Without gravity the universe would expand at the same rate forever. But as it is, all the masses in the universe attract each other — and tend to slow the expansion down.

5) The Big Bang isn't the only game in town. The 'Steady State' theory says that the universe has always existed as it is now, and it always will do. It's based on the idea that the universe appears pretty much the same everywhere. This theory explains the apparent expansion (and red-shift) by suggesting that matter is being created in the spaces as the universe expands.

In the beginning, there was — well, nobody knows, actually...

Most scientists accept the idea of the Big Bang — it's the best way to explain the evidence we have at the moment. But if new evidence turns up, the theory could turn out to be rubbish. After all, there wasn't anyone around 14 billion years ago, taking photos and writing things down in a little notebook.

Revision Summary for P1a Topics 1, 2 & 3

There's been loads of information over the last three topics. And there is really only one way to check that you've learnt it all — you guessed it, a page full of questions. So go on, have a go...

1) Describe the main features of the geocentric model.

2) Explain how Galileo's observations of Jupiter proved the geocentric model wrong.

3) How are we able to see stars? How are we able to see planets?

4)* Write down the two formulas for the speed of a wave. Find the wavelength of a wave with frequency 15 MHz and speed 3×10^8 m/s.

5) Give an example of a transverse wave. Give an example of a longitudinal wave.

6) Light is reflected off a mirror, as shown in the diagram. What is the angle a?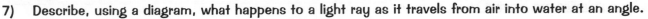

7) Describe, using a diagram, what happens to a light ray as it travels from air into water at an angle.

8) Draw a diagram to show how a converging lens works.

9) Describe what is meant by the focal point of a lens. How can you work out the focal length of a lens?

10) Briefly explain how an object's distance from a lens affects what image you will see.

11) How many converging lenses does a refracting telescope use? Explain how a refracting telescope works.

12) Draw a diagram to show how a concave mirror reflects light.

13) Explain how a reflecting telescope works.

14) List the seven types of electromagnetic radiation in order of increasing wavelength.

15) Which type of electromagnetic radiation has the highest frequency?

16) Briefly describe how Herschel discovered infrared radiation.

17) Explain why some people are worried about the effects of using mobile phones.

18) What can too much exposure to UV radiation cause? Give three ways to protect yourself from UV rays.

19) Explain why hilly areas often get poor TV and radio reception.

20) Briefly explain how an optical fibre works.

21) List five uses of infrared radiation around the home.

22) Describe briefly what happens when UV light shines on a fluorescent material.

23) Describe how X-ray imaging can help to find a fracture in someone's bone.

24) Explain why radiotherapy treatment is directed carefully only at the tumour.

25) Give one advantage of irradiating food with gamma rays over other methods of sterilising.

26) Name the three types of ionising radiation. What is ionising radiation emitted from?

27) Compare the distance between the Sun and Earth with the distance between the Earth and Moon.

28) What is a galaxy? Describe the scale of the distance between galaxies.

29) What does SETI stand for?

30) Suggest one type of information a space probe might collect.

31) Give two disadvantages of telescopes on Earth compared with space telescopes.

32) Explain why we need telescopes for other parts of the EM spectrum, as well as visible light.

33) Describe what an absorption spectrum looks like. Why does it look like this?

34) Describe the first stages of a star's formation. Where does the initial energy come from?

35) What is a 'main sequence' star? How long does it last? What happens after that?

36) What are the final two stages of a small star's life? What are the two final stages of a big star's life?

37) Explain what red-shift is. Do galaxies further away have more or less red-shift than those nearer?

38) What's the main theory for the origin of the universe? Give two important bits of evidence for it.

Ultrasound and Infrasound

Can you hear that? If not, 'that' could be <u>ultrasound</u> or <u>infrasound</u>...

Ultrasound *is Sound with* Frequencies Higher *Than 20 000 Hz*

Electrical devices can be made which produce <u>electrical oscillations</u> of <u>any frequency</u>. These can easily be converted into <u>mechanical vibrations</u> to produce <u>sound</u> waves <u>beyond the range of human hearing</u> (i.e. frequencies above 20 000 Hz). This is called <u>ultrasound</u> and it pops up all over the place.

Ultrasound Waves Get Partially Reflected *at a* Boundary Between Media

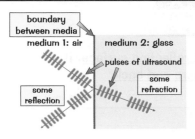

boundary between media

medium 1: air | medium 2: glass

pulses of ultrasound

some reflection | some refraction

1) When a wave passes from one medium into another, <u>some</u> of the wave is <u>reflected</u> off the boundary between the two media, and some is transmitted (and refracted — see p.73). This is <u>partial reflection</u>.

2) What this means is that you can point a pulse of ultrasound at an object, and wherever there are <u>boundaries</u> between one substance and another, some of the ultrasound gets <u>reflected back</u>.

3) The time it takes for the reflections to reach a <u>detector</u> can be used to measure <u>how far away</u> the boundary is (see next page).

Ultrasound *is Useful* in Lots of *Different Ways*

Pre-natal scanning of a foetus

1) <u>Ultrasound waves</u> can pass through the body, but whenever they reach a <u>boundary</u> between <u>two different media</u> (like fluid in the womb and the skin of the foetus) some of the wave is <u>reflected back</u> and <u>detected</u>.

2) The exact <u>timing and distribution</u> of these <u>echoes</u> are <u>processed by a computer</u> to produce a <u>video image</u> of the foetus.

3) No one knows for sure whether ultrasound is safe in all cases but <u>X-rays</u> would definitely be dangerous to the foetus.

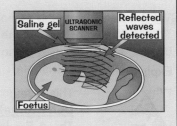

Saline gel | ULTRASONIC SCANNER | Reflected waves detected

Foetus

Sonar

1) <u>Boats</u> and <u>submarines</u> use <u>sonar</u> to detect stuff in the water around them.

2) They emit waves of <u>ultrasound</u> which <u>reflect</u> off things like other boats, the sea bed and marine animals — and <u>detect</u> these reflected waves as they arrive back at the boat.

3) Computers on-board time the <u>delay</u> between emitting the waves and detecting their reflections, and then <u>calculate how far away</u> the other objects are (p.90).

4) Animals like <u>bats</u> and <u>dolphins</u> use ultrasound to <u>sense</u> their way around their environment <u>in a similar way</u>.

5) Many animals (e.g. frogs, insects, whales and even rats) also use ultrasound frequencies to <u>communicate</u> with one another.

Infrasound *is Sound with* Frequencies Less *Than 20 Hz*

1) Sound that has a frequency <u>below</u> the range of human hearing (i.e. below <u>20 Hz</u>) is called <u>infrasound</u>.

2) Because infrasound waves have <u>long wavelengths</u>, they can travel <u>long distances</u> and <u>diffract</u> around objects easily.

3) <u>Elephants</u> use infrasound to communicate with other members of their herd over <u>long distances</u>. <u>Tigers</u> also use infrasound in their <u>growls</u> and <u>roars</u> so they can be heard by rivals or mates from <u>far away</u>.

4) Some <u>microphones</u> are sensitive enough to detect infrasound and can be used to monitor <u>animal movements</u> in remote locations.

5) <u>Meteor strikes</u> and <u>volcanic eruptions</u> produce infrasound which can be used to detect them from far away.

Barry White — the undisputed master of the low frequency note...

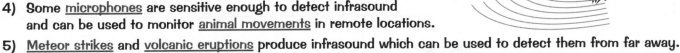

Remember — <u>infrasound</u> has a frequency <u>below 20 Hz</u> and <u>ultrasound</u> has a frequency <u>above 20 kHz</u>. Make sure you <u>learn</u> and <u>understand</u> the uses on this page too, and the exam questions on this stuff should be a doddle.

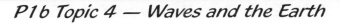

Calculating Distances Using Ultrasound

<u>Ultrasound</u> waves can be used to work out <u>distances</u>. And I'm not just telling you that as a mildly interesting fact — you might have to do it in your <u>exam</u>. So here are some <u>helpful</u> examples.

Speed = Distance ÷ Time... and DON'T FORGET the FACTOR OF 2

This is about the <u>easiest formula in Physics</u>. If you don't know it by now... well, you ought to.

$$\text{wave speed (m/s)} = \frac{\text{distance (m)}}{\text{time (s)}}$$

They'll expect you to be able to <u>use this</u> to find the <u>distance</u> to and from a <u>reflecting surface</u>, if you know both the <u>speed</u> of the wave and <u>how long</u> the wave takes to <u>travel there and back</u>.

EXAMPLE: A pulse of ultrasound takes 4.5 seconds to travel from a submarine to the sea bed and back again.

If the speed of sound in seawater is 1520 m/s, how far away is the submarine from the sea bed?

ANSWER: The formula is of course "speed = distance ÷ time" or "s = x ÷ t". We want to find the distance, x. We already know the time, 4.5 s, and the speed of sound in seawater, 1520 m/s, hence x = s × t (from the triangle).

This gives: x = 1520 × 4.5 = <u>6840 m</u>... But watch out! <u>Don't forget the factor of two for reflection questions</u>: The 4.5 s is for <u>there and back</u>, so the sea bed is only <u>half</u> that distance away, <u>3420 m</u>.

Pulse sent / Pulse back

EXAMPLE: A pregnant woman goes for a prenatal scan. A pulse of ultrasound takes 0.00005 s (0.05 ms) to be sent from a point on her stomach to the baby's head and back again.

Given that the speed of sound inside soft tissue in the body is 1540 m/s, work out the distance of the baby's head from the scanner.

Pulse sent / Pulse back

ANSWER: Speed of sound inside soft tissue in the body = 1540 m/s
You need the good old formula: speed = distance / time
— and again you have to rearrange it (formula triangle):
So, x = s × t = 1540 × 0.00005 = <u>0.077 m</u>.

(See previous page for more on ultrasound scanning.)

But remember — the wave has been <u>reflected</u>, so it's travelled <u>twice the distance</u>. So you need to <u>divide by 2</u>, which gives 0.0385 m = 3.85 cm. So the head is <u>3.85 cm</u> away from the scanner.

It's only a little maths — it won't hurt a bit...

So, <u>learn the formula</u>, practise <u>rearranging it</u> and remember the <u>factor of 2</u>. Yep, that's about it. Cover the answers to the two examples above and have a go at answering them yourself — but be careful not to have too much fun.

The Earth's Structure

No one accepted the theory of plate tectonics for ages. Almost everyone does now. How times change.

The Earth Has a Crust, Mantle, Outer and Inner Core

The Earth is almost spherical and it has a layered structure, a bit like a scotch egg. Or a peach.

1) The bit we live on, the crust, is very thin (about 20 km).

2) Below that is the mantle. The mantle has all the properties of a solid, except that it can flow very slowly. Within the mantle, radioactive decay takes place. This produces a lot of heat, which causes the mantle to flow in convection currents.

3) At the centre of the Earth is the core, which we think is made of iron and nickel. The inner core is solid but the outer core surrounding it is a liquid.

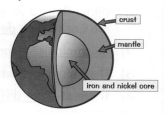

The Earth's Surface is Made Up of Tectonic Plates

1) The crust and the upper part of the mantle are cracked into a number of large pieces called tectonic plates. These plates are a bit like big rafts that 'float' on the mantle.

2) The plates don't stay in one place though. That's because the convection currents in the mantle cause the plates to drift.

3) Most of the plates are moving at speeds of a few cm per year relative to each other.

4) At plate boundaries, the plates may slide past each other — which sometimes causes earthquakes.

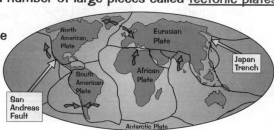

It's Difficult to Predict Earthquakes and Tsunami Waves

1) Some countries are particularly susceptible to earthquakes, which can also sometimes cause giant waves called tsunamis. Both can be extremely destructive, especially in areas where the housing isn't built to withstand them. So it would be very useful to be able to predict when they're likely to hit.

2) Unfortunately, predicting them's very hard, and scientists aren't agreed on which method works best.

3) Here's an easy experiment to show how unpredictable earthquakes can be:

- Fix sandpaper to the surface of a lab bench so that it can't be moved. Place a brick at one end of the bench on top of the sand paper. The brick and sandpaper represent tectonic plates — earthquakes happen when these plates slide suddenly against each other.

- Attach an elastic cord to the brick and join the elastic cord and the string. Tie a mass holder to the end of the string and hang it over a pulley wheel clamped to the bench.

- Gradually add masses to the mass holder. The force of the masses pulling the brick represent the forces of the convection currents in the mantle that make the tectonic plates move.

- As you continue to add masses, the brick will eventually slip to the right — this represents the earthquake.

- The thing is though, if you repeat the experiment using exactly the same equipment, it may take a different number of masses to make the brick slip each time. You can't really predict when it will happen — just like a real earthquake.

4) One way to try and predict earthquakes is to use probabilities based on previous occurrences. E.g. if a city has had earthquakes at regular intervals over the last century, that pattern may continue. This method isn't dead-on accurate, e.g. you might not get an earthquake at the exact location or exact time — maybe it'll be in the next town, or a few months late. But it still gives the area time to prepare, just in case.

Plate Tectonics — it's a smashing theory...

arthquakes — make sure you know what causes them. And remember, they're rather unpredictable — s that experiment with the brick, the sandpaper, the pulley and the masses shows.

Seismic Waves

You can't drill very far into the Earth's outer layer (only about 12 km), but luckily scientists can use the <u>seismic waves</u> produced by earthquakes to investigate the Earth's <u>inner structure</u>.

Earthquakes <u>and</u> Explosions <u>Cause</u> Seismic Waves

1) When there's an <u>earthquake</u> somewhere, it produces <u>seismic waves</u> which travel out through the Earth. We <u>detect</u> these <u>waves</u> all over the <u>surface</u> of the planet using <u>seismometers</u>.

2) <u>Seismologists</u> work out the <u>time</u> it takes for the shock waves to reach each seismometer.

3) They also note which parts of the Earth <u>don't receive the shock waves</u> at all.

4) There are <u>two different types</u> of seismic waves you need to learn — <u>P waves</u> and <u>S waves</u>:

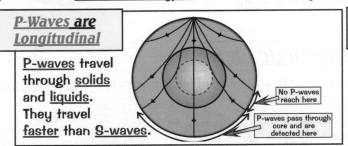

P-Waves <u>are</u> Longitudinal

<u>P-waves</u> travel through <u>solids</u> and <u>liquids</u>. They travel <u>faster</u> than <u>S-waves</u>.

No P-waves reach here

P-waves pass through core and are detected here

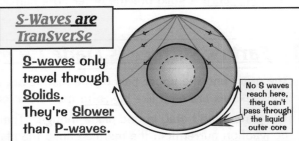

S-Waves <u>are</u> TranSverSe

<u>S-waves</u> only travel through <u>Solids</u>. They're <u>Slower</u> than <u>P-waves</u>.

No S waves reach here, they can't pass through the liquid outer core

P-waves and S-waves <u>Reflect</u> <u>and</u> <u>Refract</u>

1) When seismic waves reach a <u>boundary</u> between different layers of the Earth, some waves will be <u>reflected</u>.

2) The <u>waves</u> also change speed as the <u>properties</u> (e.g. density) of the mantle and core change. This change in speed causes the waves to change direction — which is <u>refraction</u>, of course (see page 73).

3) Most of the time the waves change speed <u>gradually</u>, resulting in a <u>curved path</u>. But when the properties change <u>suddenly</u>, the wave speed changes abruptly, and the path has a <u>kink</u>.

4) By observing how seismic waves are <u>reflected</u> and <u>refracted</u>, scientists have been able to work out <u>where</u> the <u>properties</u> of the Earth change <u>dramatically</u>. Our current understanding of the <u>internal structure</u> of the Earth is based on these <u>observations</u>.

<u>You Need to</u> <u>Understand</u> <u>the Seismometer</u> Results

1) <u>Seismometer</u> readings (<u>seismograms</u>) can be used to work out the <u>distance</u> to an earthquake's <u>epicentre</u> (the <u>point</u> on the <u>earth's surface</u> directly above the focus of the earthquake).

2) P-waves and S-waves travel at <u>different speeds</u> — so you'll usually see <u>two distinct tremors</u> on the seismogram. The <u>first one</u> is the <u>P-wave</u> and the <u>second</u> is the <u>S-wave</u> (the 'P' and 'S' are for <u>primary</u> and <u>secondary</u>).

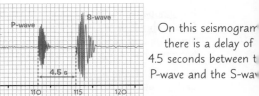

On this seismogram there is a delay of 4.5 seconds between the P-wave and the S-wave

3) Using the <u>time difference</u> between the two waves, you can calculate <u>how far away</u> the earthquake or explosion was.

4) Then you can draw a <u>circle</u> on a map <u>centred</u> on the location of your <u>seismometer</u>, with the <u>distance</u> you calculated above as its <u>radius</u>. This is called a <u>distance arc</u>.

5) The distance arcs from <u>three or more</u> seismometers will <u>all cross</u> at <u>one place</u> — this the <u>epicentre</u> of the earthquake. This method of finding the epicentre is called <u>triangulation</u>.

6) Triangulation only works if you have <u>at least three</u> seismometer distance arcs (the distance arcs from two seismometers will cross in two places).

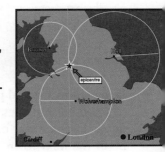

<u>What's that coming straight through the core? Is it a P-wave, Is it a P-wave?</u>

You need to remember that <u>P-waves</u> are <u>longitudinal</u> and <u>S-waves</u> are <u>transverse</u> (p.72). You might find it helpful to think of them as <u>Push-waves</u> and <u>Shake-waves</u>. Gosh — what a useful little trick. You can thank me later...

Electric Current and Power

Isn't electricity great — generally, I mean. You can power all sorts of toys and gadgets with electricity. Mind you, it'll be a pain come exam time if you don't know the basics — thankfully they're all on this page.

Electric Current is a Flow of Charge Round a Circuit

1) CURRENT is the rate of flow of charge around a circuit.
Electrons usually carry the charge — they're negatively charged particles.

2) VOLTAGE (or POTENTIAL DIFFERENCE) is an electrical pressure giving a measure of the energy transferred.

3) That might sound confusing, but try to think of current as like the flow of water around a set of pipes. Voltage is like the pressure provided by a pump which pushes the water round — if you turn up the pump and provide more pressure (or "voltage"), the flow will increase.

4) We normally say that current in a circuit flows from positive to negative. Alas, electrons were discovered long after that was decided and they turned out to be negatively charged — unlucky. This means they actually flow from –ve to +ve, opposite to the flow of "conventional current".

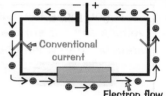
Conventional current
Electron flow

a.c. Keeps Changing Direction but d.c. Does Not

1) The mains electricity supply in your home is alternating current (a.c.). It keeps reversing its direction back and forth.

2) A CRO can show current as a trace on a graph — an a.c. trace is a wave.

3) Direct current (d.c.) is different. It always flows in the same direction.

4) The CRO trace is a horizontal line. The voltage doesn't vary — so the current has a constant value too.

5) You get direct current from batteries and solar cells (see p.97).

peak voltage
a.c.   d.c.
voltage
Cathode-ray oscilloscope (CRO) traces.

Electrical Power is the Energy Transferred per Second

1) Electrical appliances are useful because they take in electrical energy and convert it into other forms of energy, e.g. a light bulb turns electrical energy into light (and heat) energy.

2) The electrical power of an appliance tells you how quickly it transfers electrical energy.

> **ELECTRICAL POWER is the Energy Transferred per Second.**

3) The units of power are watts (W). The higher the power of your appliance, the more energy is transferred every second. So a 100 W light bulb is brighter than a 60 W bulb.

Measuring the Current and Voltage Can Tell You the Power

You can calculate the power of any component in a circuit using this nice n' simple experiment:

1) Make a circuit with an ammeter, switch, battery and your test component (e.g. a resistor) in series — this means they're all in one loop. The ammeter will measure the current flowing through the circuit.

2) Connect a voltmeter in parallel, across the component you're investigating. The voltmeter will measure the voltage across the component.

3) Close the switch to complete the circuit — you'll see a reading on both the ammeter and voltmeter. Record these numbers then use them to calculate the power of the component using this formula:

battery
switch →
test component →
V
voltmeter
A ← ammeter

Power = Current × Voltage
(watts, W) (amps, A) (volts, V)

EXAMPLE: A current of 0.2 A flows through a lamp when it is connected to a 3 V battery. Calculate the power of the lamp.
ANSWER: P = I × V = 0.2 × 3 = 0.6 W

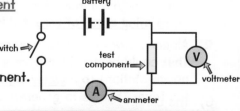

$$P = I \times V$$

a.c. = wiggly   d.c. = straight

Learn the differences between a.c. and d.c.. Also, make sure you can spell current correctly.

Generating Electricity

Generators (e.g. in power stations) use something called electromagnetic induction to make electricity. It's a bit mysterious, but don't get bogged down — there's not that much to it.

Moving a Magnet in a Coil of Wire Induces a Voltage

1) You can induce (create) a voltage, and maybe a current, in a conductor by moving a magnet in or near a coil of wire. This is called electromagnetic induction.

2) As you move the magnet, the magnetic field through the coil changes — this change in the magnetic field induces a voltage, and a current flows in the wire (if it's part of a complete circuit).

3) The direction of the voltage and current depends on which way you move the magnet:

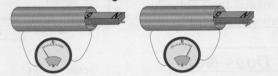

If you move the magnet into the coil the voltage and current are induced in the opposite direction from when you move it out of the coil.

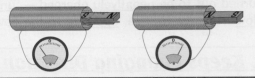

If you reverse the magnet's North-South polarity — so that the opposite pole points into the coil, the voltage and current are induced in the opposite direction.

4) You can also create a voltage and current in a conductor by either rotating a magnet in or near a coil of wire, or by rotating a coil of wire in a magnetic field (see below).

Four Factors Affect the Size of the Induced Voltage and Current

1) If you want a bigger peak voltage (and current) you have to increase at least one of these four things:

> 1) The **STRENGTH** of the **MAGNET**   2) The **AREA** of the **COIL**
> 3) The number of **TURNS** on the **COIL**   4) The **SPEED** of movement

2) To reduce the voltage, you would reduce one of those factors, obviously.

3) If you move or turn the magnet faster, you'll get a higher peak voltage, but also get a higher frequency — because the magnetic field is reversing more frequently.

faster turns

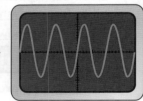

This is How All Generators Work

1) Generators generate alternating current (a.c.) by electromagnetic induction, either by rotating a magnet or by rotating a coil of wire and keeping the magnet fixed.

2) All generators just need something to do the turning. That could be anything from a steam-driven turbine (like in a power station) to a water-wheel (like the one the Queen's got in the River Thames to generate electricity for her pad at Windsor).

3) A dynamo is a particular type of generator which is often used on bikes to power the lights. Here the magnet is rotated instead of the coil. The dynamo is attached to a wheel — so as you turn the wheels, you're turning the magnet inside the dynamo.

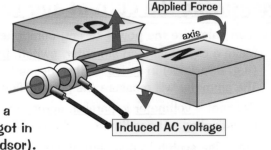

Applied Force

axis

Induced AC voltage

So THAT's how they make electricity — I always wondered...

The National Grid (see p.99) is fed by hundreds of generators — mostly powered by burning things to make steam, which turns a turbine, which turns a coil in a magnetic field. More on that coming up next...

Non-Renewable Energy and Power Stations

There are 12 different types of energy resource.
They fit into two broad types: renewable and non-renewable.

Non-Renewable Energy Resources Will Run Out One Day

The non-renewables are the three FOSSIL FUELS and NUCLEAR:

1) Coal
2) Oil
3) Natural gas
4) Nuclear fuels (uranium and plutonium)

> a) They will all 'run out' one day.
> b) They all do damage to the environment.
> c) But they provide most of our energy.

There are Environmental Problems with Using Non-Renewables

1) All three fossil fuels (coal, oil and natural gas) release CO_2. For the same amount of energy produced, coal releases the most CO_2, followed by oil then natural gas. All this CO_2 adds to the greenhouse effect, and causes global warming. We could stop some of it entering the atmosphere — by 'capturing' it and burying it underground, for instance — but the technology is too expensive to be widely used yet.

2) Burning coal and oil releases sulfur dioxide, which causes acid rain.
This is reduced by taking the sulfur out before it's burned, or cleaning up the emissions.

3) Coal mining makes a mess of the landscape, especially "open-cast mining".

4) Oil spillages cause serious environmental problems. We try to avoid them, but they'll always happen.

5) Nuclear power is clean but the nuclear waste is very dangerous and difficult to dispose of.

6) Nuclear fuel (i.e. uranium) is relatively cheap but the overall cost of nuclear power is high due to the cost to build and decommission the power plant.

7) Nuclear power always carries the risk of a major catastrophe like the Chernobyl disaster.

Most Power Stations Use Steam to Drive a Turbine

Most of the electricity we use is generated from the four NON-RENEWABLE sources of energy (coal, oil, natural gas and nuclear) in big power stations, which are all pretty much the same apart from the boiler. Learn the basic features of the typical power station shown here and also the nuclear reactor below.

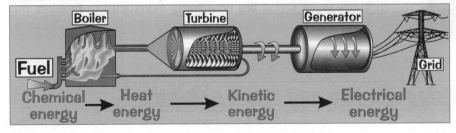

They said turbine, Dave.

Nuclear Reactors Are Just Fancy Boilers

1) A nuclear power station is mostly the same as the one above, where nuclear fission produces heat to make steam to drive turbines, etc. The difference is in the boiler, as shown here:

2) Nuclear power stations take the longest time of all the power stations to start up. Natural gas power stations take the shortest time.

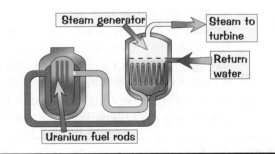

It all boils down to steam...

Steam engines were invented as long ago as the 17th century, and yet we're still using that idea to produce most of our electricity today, over 300 years later. Amazing...

Using Renewable Energy Resources

Renewable energy sources could solve all our problems when the fossil fuels run out — but there are lots of them to remember. Here are a couple of pages to talk you through the important ones. Enjoy.

Renewable Energy Resources Will Never Run Out

a) A renewable energy source is one that will never run out.

b) Most of them do damage the environment, but in less nasty ways than non-renewables.

c) Sadly they don't all provide much energy and some of them are unreliable as they depend on the weather.

Hydroelectricity — Building Dams and Flooding Valleys

1) Hydroelectric power usually involves flooding a valley by building a big dam.

2) Rainwater is caught and allowed out through turbines.

3) There is a big impact on the environment due to the flooding of the valley and possible loss of habitat for some species.

4) A big advantage is immediate response to increased electricity demand — more water can be let out through the turbines to generate more electricity.

5) Initial costs are often high but there are minimal running costs and it's a reliable energy source.

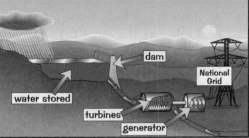

Wave Power — Lots of Little Wave Powered Turbines

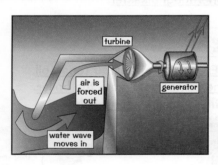

1) Waves can provide an up and down motion which can be used use to drive a generator.

2) Wave power is fairly unreliable, since waves tend to die out when the wind drops.

3) Most electricity generated from wave power uses waves close to the shore. Waves further out in the ocean are much more powerful — offshore wave farms are now being developed to harness this power.

4) Wave power is never likely to provide energy on a large scale but it can be useful on small islands.

Tidal Barrages — Using the Sun and Moon's Gravity

1) Tidal barrages are big dams built across river estuaries, with turbines in them.

2) As the tide comes in it fills up the estuary to a height of several metres. This water can then be allowed out through turbines at a controlled speed. It also drives the turbines on the way in.

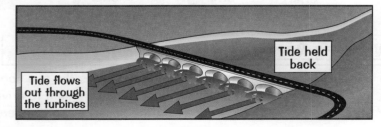

3) Even though it can only be used in a few of the most suitable estuaries, tidal power is a reliable energy source that has the potential to generate a significant amount of energy.

I thought you weren't supposed to mix water and electricity...

Wherever water is moving, you can use it to turn a turbine. The renewable energy sources on this page all involve a flow of water turning a turbine, but they're not the same. Make sure you understand the differences between them and how each one works. Renewable energy is awesome — luckily for you there's a whole other page on it.

Using Renewable Energy Resources

As promised, here's the <u>second</u> page on those lovely, clean, <u>green</u>, renewable energy sources. If it's all getting a bit too much, <u>don't worry</u> — the next page is a bit of a <u>recap</u> to compare <u>all</u> the different energy sources.

Wind Power — Lots of Little Wind Turbines

1) Each wind turbine has its own <u>generator</u> inside it so the electricity is generated <u>directly</u> from the <u>wind</u> turning the <u>blades</u>, which <u>turn the generator</u>.

2) There's <u>no pollution</u> (except for a little bit when they're manufactured).

3) But they do <u>spoil the view</u> and they can be <u>very noisy</u>, which is annoying for people living nearby.

4) They <u>only</u> work when it's <u>windy</u>, so it's not always <u>possible</u> to <u>supply</u> more electricity when there's <u>extra demand</u>.

Solar Cells Generate Electric Currents Directly From Sunlight

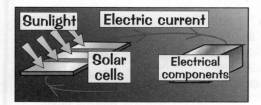

1) Solar cells are usually used to generate electricity on a <u>relatively small scale</u>.

2) Solar power is often used in <u>remote places</u> where there aren't many other ways to generate electricity, and in satellites.

3) In sunny countries solar power is a <u>very reliable source</u> of energy — but only in the <u>daytime</u>. Solar power can still be cost-effective even in <u>cloudy countries</u> like Britain.

Geothermal Energy — Heat from Underground

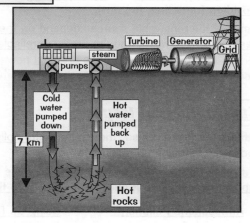

1) This is <u>only possible</u> in <u>certain places</u> where <u>hot rocks</u> lie quite near to the <u>surface</u>. The source of much of the heat is the <u>slow decay</u> of various <u>radioactive elements</u>, including <u>uranium</u>, deep inside the Earth.

2) <u>Water is pumped</u> in pipes down to the <u>hot rocks</u> and it <u>returns as steam</u> to drive a <u>generator</u>.

3) This is actually <u>brilliant 'free' energy</u> with no real environmental problems.

4) The only big drawbacks are the <u>high setup cost</u> and the fact that there are <u>very few places</u> where this seems to be an <u>economic option</u> (for now).

Biomass Is Natural Waste That Can Be Burnt to Produce Electricity

1) Biomass can be anything from <u>farm waste</u>, <u>animal droppings</u> and <u>landfill rubbish</u> to <u>specially grown forests</u>.

2) The waste material is <u>burnt</u> in power stations to <u>drive turbines</u> and produce <u>electricity</u>. Or sometimes it's <u>fermented</u> to produce other fuels such as '<u>biogas</u>' (usually <u>methane</u>) or <u>ethanol</u>.

3) The <u>plants</u> that grew to <u>produce the waste</u> (or to <u>feed the animals</u> that produced the dung) would have <u>absorbed carbon dioxide</u> from the atmosphere as they were growing. When the waste is burnt this CO_2 is <u>re-released</u> into the <u>atmosphere</u>. So using biomass to generate electricity has <u>no overall effect</u> on <u>atmospheric CO_2 levels</u> — so it's <u>carbon neutral</u>. (Although this only really works if you keep growing plants at the same rate you're burning things.)

The power that you're supplying — it's electrifying...

here's a lot to take in on these two pages but <u>don't panic</u> — it's all pretty straightforward. Make sure you've nderstood them before you move on to the next one though, as that's about <u>comparing</u> different energy sources.

Comparison of Energy Resources

Setting Up a Power Station

Because coal and oil are running out fast, many old <u>coal- and oil-fired power stations</u> are being <u>taken out of use</u>. Often they're being <u>replaced</u> by <u>gas-fired power stations</u> because these are <u>quick</u> to <u>set up</u>, there's still quite a lot of <u>gas left</u> and gas <u>doesn't pollute as badly</u> as coal and oil.

But gas is <u>not</u> the <u>only option</u>, as you really ought to know if you've been concentrating at all over the last few pages.

When looking at the options for a <u>new power station</u>, there are <u>several factors</u> to consider: How much it <u>costs</u> to set up and run, <u>how long</u> it takes to <u>build</u>, <u>how much power</u> it can generate, etc. Then there are also the trickier factors like <u>damage to the environment</u> and <u>impact on local communities</u>. And because these are often <u>very contentious</u> issues, getting <u>permission</u> to build certain types of power station can be a <u>long-running</u> process, and hence <u>increase</u> the overall <u>set-up time</u>.

Set-Up Costs

<u>Renewable</u> resources often need <u>bigger power stations</u> than non-renewables for the <u>same output</u>. And as you'd expect, the <u>bigger</u> the power station, the <u>more expensive</u>.

<u>Nuclear reactors</u> and <u>hydroelectric dams</u> also need <u>huge</u> amounts of <u>engineering</u> to make them <u>safe</u>, which bumps up the cost.

Reliability Issues

All the <u>non-renewables</u> are <u>reliable energy providers</u> (until they run out).

Many of the <u>renewable</u> sources <u>depend on the weather</u>, which means they're pretty <u>unreliable</u> here in the UK. The <u>exceptions</u> are <u>tidal</u> power and <u>geothermal</u> (which <u>don't</u> depend on weather).

Environmental Issues

If there's a <u>fuel</u> involved, there'll be <u>waste pollution</u> and you'll be <u>using up resources</u>.

If it <u>relies on the weather</u>, it's often got to be in an <u>exposed place</u> where it sticks out like a <u>sore thumb</u>.

Atmospheric Pollution
Coal, Oil, Gas, Biomass
(+ others, though less so)

Visual Pollution
Coal, Oil, Gas, Nuclear, Tidal, Waves, Wind, Hydroelectric, Biomass

Other Problems
Nuclear (dangerous waste, explosions, contamination), Hydroelectric (dams bursting)

Using Up Resources
Coal, Oil, Gas, Nuclear

Noise Pollution
Coal, Oil, Gas, Nuclear, Wind, Biomass

Disruption of Wildlife Habitats
Hydroelectric, Tidal

Set-Up Time

This is affected by the <u>size</u> of the power station, the <u>complexity</u> of the engineering and also the <u>planning issues</u> (e.g. <u>discussions</u> over whether they should be <u>allowed</u> to build a nuclear power station on a stretch of <u>beautiful coastline</u> can last <u>years</u>).

<u>Gas</u> is one of the <u>quickest</u> to set up.

Running/ Fuel Costs

<u>Renewables</u> usually have the <u>lowest running costs</u>, because there's <u>no</u> actual <u>fuel</u> involved (except biomass).

Location Issues

This is fairly <u>common sense</u> — a <u>power station</u> has to be <u>near</u> to the <u>stuff it runs on</u>.

<u>Solar</u> — pretty much <u>anywhere</u>, though the sunnier the better

<u>Gas</u> — pretty much <u>anywhere</u> there's piped gas (most of the UK)

<u>Biomass</u> — pretty much <u>anywhere</u>

<u>Hydroelectric</u> — <u>hilly</u>, <u>rainy</u> places with <u>floodable valleys</u>, e.g. the Lake District, Scottish Highlands

<u>Wind</u> — <u>exposed</u>, <u>windy</u> places like moors and coasts or out at sea

<u>Oil</u> — near the <u>coast</u> (oil transported by sea)

<u>Waves</u> — on the <u>coast</u>

<u>Coal</u> — near <u>coal mines</u>, e.g. Yorkshire, Wales

<u>Nuclear</u> — <u>away from people</u> (in case of disaster), <u>near water</u> (for cooling)

<u>Tidal</u> — big <u>river estuaries</u> where a dam can be built

<u>Geothermal</u> — fairly limited, only in places where <u>hot rocks</u> are <u>near the Earth's surface</u>

Of course — the biggest problem is we demand too much electricity...

It would be lovely if we could get rid of all the <u>nasty polluting power stations</u> and replace them all with clean, green energy, just like that... but it's not quite that simple. Renewable energy has its <u>own problems</u> too, and probably isn't enough to power the <u>whole country</u> without having a wind farm in everyone's back yard.

Electricity and the National Grid

The <u>National Grid</u> is the <u>network</u> of pylons and cables that covers <u>the whole of Britain</u>, getting electricity to homes everywhere. Whoever you pay for your electricity, it's the National Grid that gets it to you.

Electricity Gets Around *via the* National Grid...

1) The <u>National Grid</u> takes electrical energy from the <u>power stations</u> to just where it's needed in <u>homes</u> and <u>industry</u>.

2) It enables power to be <u>generated</u> anywhere on the grid, and then be <u>supplied</u> anywhere else on the grid.

3) To transmit the <u>huge</u> amount of <u>power</u> needed, you need either a <u>high voltage</u> or a <u>high current</u> (see page 93).

4) The <u>problem</u> with a <u>high current</u> is that you <u>lose loads of energy</u> through <u>heat</u> in the cables.

5) It's much <u>cheaper</u> to <u>boost the voltage</u> up <u>really high</u> (to 400 000 V — eeek!) and keep the current <u>very low</u>.

...*With a Little Help from* Pylons *and* Transformers

1) To get the voltage to 400 000 V to transmit power requires <u>transformers</u> as well as <u>big pylons</u> with <u>huge insulators</u> — but it's <u>still cheaper</u>.

2) The transformers have to <u>step</u> the <u>alternating</u> voltage <u>up</u> at one end, for <u>efficient transmission</u>, and then bring it back down to <u>safe, useable levels</u> at the other end.

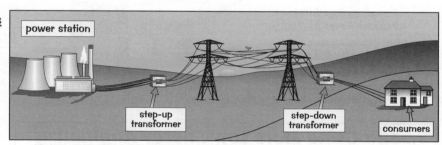

3) Transformers all have two coils, the <u>primary</u> and the <u>secondary</u>, joined with an <u>iron core</u>.

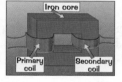

4) The <u>voltage</u> is <u>increased</u> ('<u>stepped up</u>') using a <u>step-up transformer</u>. They have <u>more</u> turns on the <u>secondary</u> coil than the primary coil.

5) It's then <u>reduced</u> again ('<u>stepped down</u>') at the consumer end using a <u>step-down transformer</u>. They have <u>more</u> turns on the <u>primary</u> coil than the secondary.

6) You can calculate the <u>output voltage</u> from a transformer if you know the <u>input voltage</u> and the number of <u>turns</u> on each coil:

$$\frac{\text{Primary Voltage}}{\text{Secondary Voltage}} = \frac{\text{Number of turns on Primary}}{\text{Number of turns on Secondary}}$$

You can use the equation either way up...

$$\frac{V_P}{V_S} = \frac{N_P}{N_S} \quad \text{or} \quad \frac{V_S}{V_P} = \frac{N_S}{N_P}$$

There are Problems *with Transmitting Such* Huge Amounts of Energy

1) Even at high voltages, electricity transmission <u>isn't very efficient</u>, so <u>power losses are high</u>.

2) The high voltage is a <u>risk to people</u> — e.g. flying a <u>kite</u> into a <u>power line</u> in the rain could be <u>fatal</u>.

3) Some people are <u>worried</u> about the effects on longer-term <u>health</u> of people <u>living near</u> power lines. Links with <u>leukaemia</u> have been suggested, though studies haven't yet found any conclusive evidence.

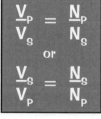

400 000 V — you wouldn't want to fly your kite into that...

you had your <u>own</u> solar panel or wind generator, you could <u>sell back</u> any surplus electricity to the <u>National</u> rid. So if you don't use much electricity, but you generate a lot of it, you can actually <u>make money</u> instead of pending it. Nice trick if you can do it. Shame solar panels cost a fortune...

Energy Efficiency & Cost-Efficiency

You Can Save Money by Insulating Your House...

1) If you want to save money on heating bills you can insulate your house — but it costs money to install insulation.

2) Eventually, though, the money you save on your heating bills will equal the initial cost of the insulation — the time this takes is called the payback time. After that you'll save money every year. It's a good idea to work out the payback time before you spend your money, to see if the insulation will be cost-efficient.

3) Cheaper methods of insulation are usually less effective at saving energy — so they save you less money per year. But they often have short payback times, so they're more cost-efficient.

4) If you look at it over, say, a five-year period then a cheap hot water tank jacket wins over expensive double glazing.

Loft Insulation
Fibreglass 'wool' laid across the loft floor and ceiling.
Initial Cost: £200
Annual Saving: £100
Payback Time: 2 years

Hot Water Tank Jacket
Lagging such as fibreglass wool.
Initial Cost: £60
Annual Saving: £15
Payback Time: 4 years

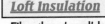

$$\text{payback time (in years)} = \frac{\text{initial cost}}{\text{annual saving}}$$

Cavity Walls & Insulation
Two layers of bricks with insulating foam squirted into the gap.
Initial Cost: £150
Annual Saving: £100
Payback Time: 18 months

Double Glazing
Two layers of glass with an air gap.
Initial Cost: £2400
Annual Saving: £80
Payback Time: 30 years

Thick Curtains
Initial Cost: £180
Annual Saving: £20
Payback Time: 9 years

Draught-Proofing
Strips of foam and plastic around doors and windows.
Initial Cost: £100
Annual Saving: £15
Payback Time: nearly 7 years

...and Using More Low-Energy Appliances

Low-energy and efficient appliances will be cheaper to run, but they're often more expensive to buy — you might need to do some maths to work out payback time and cost-efficiency.

EXAMPLE: Maria is choosing a new fridge. Fridge A costs £400 and will save her approximately 19p a day to run compared to her old fridge. Fridge B costs £325 but would only save her 13p a day to run. Which fridge will have the shorter payback time?

ANSWER: Fridge A: annual saving = £0.19 × 365 days = £69.35
Fridge A: payback time = initial cost ÷ annual saving = £400 ÷ £69.35 = 5.77 years
Fridge B: annual saving = £0.13 × 365 days = £47.45
Fridge B: payback time = initial cost ÷ annual saving = £325 ÷ £47.45 = 6.85 years
5.77 years < 6.85 years, so Fridge A has the shorter payback time.

Energy Can be Measured in Joules or Kilowatt-Hours

1) Energy is normally measured in joules (J) or kilojoules (kJ). 1 kJ = 1000 J.

2) The amount of energy an appliance uses depends on its power and the time you leave it on for. The power of an appliance can be worked out using this equation:

$$\text{POWER (in W)} = \frac{\text{ENERGY (in J)}}{\text{TIME (in s)}}$$

3) Electricity meters record how much energy you've used, not in joules, but in "kilowatt-hours" (kWh). A kilowatt-hour is the amount of energy used by a 1 kW (1 kW = 1000 W) appliance left on for 1 hour.

4) You can work out the cost of using an appliance with the equation on the right. You might have to rearrange it too.

$$\text{COST} = \text{POWER (in kW)} \times \text{TIME (in hours)} \times \text{COST of 1 kWh}$$

Save energy — stay in bed...

When you're dealing with power, time and energy, you normally use the standard units — watts, seconds and joules. When you're talking about the cost of energy, you have to use kilowatts, hours and kWh. Don't forget.

Energy Transfer

Thermal (heat) energy is just one type of energy, but there are lots more as well:

Learn These Nine Types of Energy

You should know all of these well enough by now to list them from memory, including the examples:

1) ELECTRICAL Energy...................................... — whenever a current flows.
2) LIGHT Energy... — from the Sun, light bulbs, etc.
3) SOUND Energy.. — from loudspeakers or anything noisy.
4) KINETIC Energy, or MOVEMENT Energy...... — anything that's moving has it.
5) NUCLEAR Energy....................................... — released only from nuclear reactions.
6) THERMAL Energy or HEAT Energy............. — flows from hot objects to colder ones.
7) GRAVITATIONAL POTENTIAL Energy............... — possessed by anything which can fall.
8) ELASTIC POTENTIAL Energy........................ — stretched springs, elastic, rubber bands, etc.
9) CHEMICAL Energy...................................... — possessed by foods, fuels, batteries etc.

Potential- and Chemical- Are Forms of Stored Energy

The last three above are forms of stored energy because the energy is not obviously doing anything, it's kind of waiting to happen, i.e. waiting to be turned into one of the other forms.

The Principle of the Conservation of Energy is Really Important

Many of our ideas about energy and the universe are based around the principle of the conservation of energy:

ENERGY CAN NEVER BE CREATED NOR DESTROYED — IT'S ONLY EVER TRANSFERRED FROM ONE FORM TO ANOTHER.

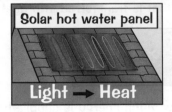

Solar hot water panel
Light → Heat

falling object
Gravitational Potential → Kinetic

ELECTRICAL DEVICES CONVERT ELECTRICAL ENERGY INTO SOUND, LIGHT, HEAT, ETC.

(and, of course, a bit of wasted heat)

Microphone/amplifier/speaker
Sound → Electrical → Sound

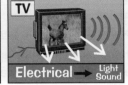

TV
Electrical → Light Sound

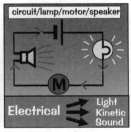

circuit/lamp/motor/speaker
Electrical → Light Kinetic Sound

BATTERIES CONVERT CHEMICAL ENERGY TO ELECTRICAL TO RUN ELECTRIC DEVICES

(and, of course, there's a bit of wasted heat)

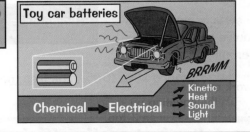

Toy car batteries
BRRMM
Chemical → Electrical → Kinetic Heat Sound Light

Energy can't be created or destroyed — only talked about a lot...*

Chemical energy → kinetic energy → electrical energy → kinetic energy → chemical energy.
(me thinking)   (me typing)   (my computer)   (printing machine)   (you reading this)

* The less well-known "Principle of Conversation of Energy".

Energy Transformations

'Efficiency' is a word that's bandied about a lot in <u>everyday</u> conversations, but in <u>physics</u> it has a <u>specific</u> meaning. Read on and judge for yourself how <u>efficient</u> your <u>revision</u> time has been.

All Machines Waste Some Energy

1) Electrical appliances are just one kind of <u>machine</u>. Machines <u>convert energy</u> from <u>one form</u> to <u>another</u>. Take cars for instance — you put in <u>chemical energy</u> (petrol, diesel or LPG) and the engine converts it into <u>kinetic (movement) energy</u>.

2) The <u>total energy output</u> is always the <u>same</u> as the <u>energy input</u>, but only some of the output energy is <u>useful</u>.

3) This is because some of the <u>input energy</u> is always <u>lost</u> or <u>wasted</u>, often as <u>heat</u>. In a car, some of the chemical energy is converted into <u>heat and sound energy</u>. This is wasted energy — although you could always stick your dinner under the bonnet and warm it up on the drive home.

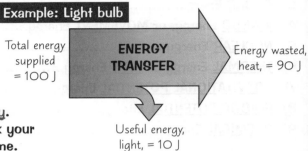

Example: Light bulb

Total energy supplied = 100 J

ENERGY TRANSFER

Energy wasted, heat, = 90 J

Useful energy, light, = 10 J

4) When you <u>charge up</u> your <u>mobile phone</u> or <u>MP3 player</u>, the charger can only convert a small amount of <u>electrical energy</u> into <u>chemical energy</u> in the device's <u>battery</u>. Most of the energy is lost as <u>heat</u> — think about how <u>warm</u> your <u>charger</u> gets if you've left it on for a long time.

5) The <u>less energy</u> that is <u>wasted</u>, the <u>more</u> <u>efficient</u> the machine is said to be.

More Efficient Devices Waste Less Energy

The <u>efficiency</u> of a device tells you the <u>proportion</u> of the <u>energy input</u> that is transferred into <u>useful energy</u>.

$$\text{Efficiency} = \frac{\text{USEFUL Energy OUTPUT}}{\text{TOTAL Energy INPUT}} \times 100\%$$

1) So, to work out the efficiency of a machine, you need to know how much energy is <u>supplied</u> to the device — the <u>Total Energy INPUT</u>.

2) Then find how much <u>useful energy</u> the machine <u>transfers</u> — the <u>Useful Energy OUTPUT</u>. The question might tell you this directly or it might tell you how much energy is <u>wasted</u>.

3) Then just <u>divide</u> the <u>smaller number</u> by the <u>bigger one</u> to get a value for <u>efficiency</u> somewhere between <u>0 and 100%</u>. Easy. BUT... If your answer is bigger than 100%, you've probably done the division <u>upside down</u>.

Electric kettle

180 000 J of electrical energy supplied

9000 J of heat given out <u>to the room</u>

Think about it!

$$\text{Efficiency} = \frac{\text{Useful En. Out}}{\text{Total En. In}} \times 100\% = \frac{171\,000}{180\,000} \times 100\% = 95\%$$

4) The closer the efficiency is to 100%, the <u>less money</u> you'll waste paying for energy you can't use.

I'm not lazy — I'm just really efficient...

Efficiency is one of those things that'll come up <u>again</u> and <u>again</u>. If I were you, I wouldn't even think about going into the exam without knowing that <u>equation</u> inside out — it's a really <u>important</u> one. It's useful to remember that <u>electric heaters</u> are usually the <u>most efficient</u> machines as all the electricity is converted to "<u>useful</u>" heat.

Heat Radiation

Be careful not to get confused between <u>heat radiation</u> and <u>ionising radiation</u> (see page 81). This page is all about <u>heat energy</u> and the types of <u>materials</u> that are good at <u>absorbing</u> and <u>emitting</u> it.

Thermal Radiation Involves Emission of Electromagnetic Waves

<u>Heat radiation</u> consists purely of electromagnetic waves of a certain range of frequencies — <u>infrared radiation</u>. It's next to visible light in the <u>electromagnetic spectrum</u> (see p.76).

1) <u>All objects</u> are <u>continually</u> emitting and absorbing <u>heat radiation</u>.

2) An object that's <u>hotter</u> than its surroundings <u>emits more radiation</u> than it <u>absorbs</u> (as it <u>cools</u> down). And an object that's <u>cooler</u> than its surroundings <u>absorbs more radiation</u> than it <u>emits</u> (as it <u>warms</u> up).

3) <u>Power</u> is the just the <u>rate of energy change</u> — that's energy ÷ time (see p.100). For an object to stay at the <u>same</u> temperature, the <u>power</u> of heat <u>absorbed</u> needs to be the <u>same</u> as the power <u>emitted</u>.

4) You can <u>feel</u> this <u>heat radiation</u> if you stand near something <u>hot</u> like a fire or if you put your hand just above the bonnet of a recently parked car.

(recently parked car)

(after an hour or so)

Radiation Depends an Awful Lot on Surface Colour and Texture

1) <u>Dark matt</u> surfaces <u>absorb</u> heat radiation falling on them much <u>better</u> than <u>bright glossy</u> surfaces, such as <u>gloss white</u> or <u>silver</u>. They also <u>emit much more</u> heat radiation (at any given temperature).

2) <u>Silvered</u> surfaces <u>reflect</u> nearly all heat radiation falling on them.

Solar hot water panels

1) <u>Solar hot water panels</u> contain <u>water pipes</u> under a <u>black surface</u> (or black painted pipes under glass).

2) <u>Heat radiation</u> from the Sun is <u>absorbed</u> by the <u>black surface</u> to <u>heat the water</u> in the pipes.

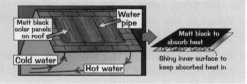

Survival Blankets

1) If someone gets injured halfway up a big snowy hill, it can be <u>crucial</u> to <u>keep them</u> as <u>warm</u> as possible till help arrives.

2) A <u>silver coloured blanket</u> helps to <u>stop</u> their body <u>heat radiating away</u> — and could save their life.

There Are Lots of Fairly Dull Experiments to Demonstrate This...

Here are two of the most gripping:

Leslie's Cube

The <u>matt black</u> side <u>emits most heat</u>, so it's that thermometer which gets <u>hottest</u>.

The Melting Wax Trick

The <u>matt black</u> surface <u>absorbs most heat</u>, so its wax <u>melts</u> first and the ball bearing <u>drops</u>.

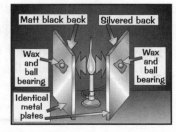

know it's Leslie's Cube — but he said I could borrow it...

he key idea here is that <u>heat radiation</u> is affected by the <u>colour</u> and <u>texture</u> of surfaces. Thermal radiation uestions often ask you <u>why</u> something's painted silver, or how you could <u>reduce the heat losses</u> from something.

Revision Summary for P1b Topics 4, 5 & 6

Well, here we are again. It's time for another round of questions. You've probably had enough of me wittering on by now — so I'll leave you to get stuck in. Good luck, chaps.

1) What is ultrasound? Describe how sonar works.

2) Explain why ultrasound rather than X-rays is used to take images of a foetus.

3) What is infrasound? What are the advantages of using sounds with long wavelengths?

4) Suggest two situations in which scientists might use microphones that are sensitive to infrasound.

5) What are tectonic plates? Why do they move? What can these movements cause?

6) Are predictions of earthquakes based on previous tectonic activity reliable? Why?

7) How do P-waves and S-waves differ regarding: a) type of wave b) speed   c) what they go through?

8) Describe how scientists use information from seismographs to calculate the distance to an earthquake.

9) Why are three (or more) seismometers needed to identify the exact location of an earthquake?

10) Describe the difference between a.c. and d.c..

11)* Draw a diagram of a circuit that you could use to work out the power of a motor.
    What equation would you use to do the calculation?

12) Describe how a voltage can be induced using a magnet and a coil of wire.

13) What is meant by a non-renewable energy resource?
    Name four different non-renewable energy resources.

14) Explain how electricity is generated in a gas-fired power station.

15) State one advantage and two disadvantages of using renewable energy resources.

16) Describe how the following renewable energy resources are used to generate electricity:
    a) waves   b) the tide   c) wind   d) solar energy   e) geothermal energy   f) biomass

17) Name six factors that need to be considered when setting up a power station.

18) Explain why a very high voltage is used to transmit electricity in the National Grid.

19)* The following table gives some information about two different light bulbs.
    a) What is the payback time for bulb A?
    b) Which bulb is more cost-efficient?
    c) Bulb A is rated at 0.1 kW. If one unit of electricity costs 8p,
       how much will it cost if the bulb is left on for 5 hours?

	Price of bulb	Annual saving
Bulb A	£2.50	£1.25
Bulb B	£3.00	£2.00

20) Name nine types of energy and give an example of each.

21) Give two examples of forms of stored energy.

22) State the principle of the conservation of energy.

23) The useful energy output of a device is usually much less than the
    total energy input. What happens to the rest of this energy?

24) Write down the formula for calculating efficiency.

25)*What is the efficiency of a motor that converts 100 J
    of electrical energy into 70 J of useful kinetic energy?

26) True or false — an object that's hotter than its surroundings emits more radiation than it absorbs.

27) Explain why solar hot water panels have a matt black surface.

28) Describe an experiment to demonstrate how the colour or texture
    of a material affects the amount of heat energy that it absorbs.

The Perfect Cup of Tea

The making and drinking of tea are important life skills. It's not something that will crop up in the exam, but it is something that will make your revision much easier. So here's a guide to making the perfect cuppa...

1) Choose the Right Mug

A good mug is an essential part of the tea drinking experience, but choosing the right vessel for your tea can be tricky. Here's a guide to choosing your mug:

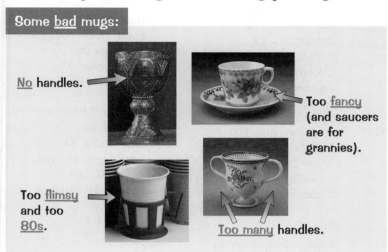

Some bad mugs:

No handles.

Too fancy (and saucers are for grannies).

Too flimsy and too 80s.

Too many handles.

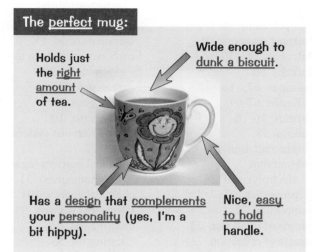

The perfect mug:

Holds just the right amount of tea.

Wide enough to dunk a biscuit.

Has a design that complements your personality (yes, I'm a bit hippy).

Nice, easy to hold handle.

2) Get Some Water and Boil It

For a really great brew follow these easy step-by-step instructions:

1) First, pour some water into a kettle and switch it on. (Check it's switched on at the wall too.)

2) Let the kettle boil. While you're waiting, see what's on TV later and check your belly button for fluff. Oh, and put a tea bag in a mug.

3) Once the kettle has boiled, pour the water into the mug.

4) Mash the tea bag about a bit with a spoon. Remove the tea bag.

5) Add a splash of milk (and a lump of sugar or two if you're feeling naughty).

Top tea tip no. 23: why not ask your mum if she wants a cup too?

Note: some people may tell you to add the milk before the tea. Scientists have recently confirmed that this is nonsense.

3) Sit Back and Relax

Now this is important — once you've made your cuppa:

1) Have a quick rummage in the kitchen cupboards for a cheeky biscuit. (Custard creams are best — steer clear of any ginger biscuits — they're evil.)

2) Find your favourite armchair/beanbag. Move the cat.

3) Sit back and enjoy your mug of tea. You've earned it.

Phew — time for a brew I reckon...

It's best to ignore what other people say about making cups of tea and follow this method. Trust me, this is the most definitive and effective method. If you don't do it this way, you'll have a shoddy drinking experience. There, you've been warned. Now go and get the kettle on. Mine's milk and two sugars...

Index

Index

Index and Answers

Answers

Revision Summary for B1 Topic 1 (page 19)

8) E.g. 1. Does it have a shell?
   - Yes — it's a snail
   - No — go to question 2.
2. Does it have legs?
   - No — it's a worm
   - Yes — go to question 3.
3. Does it have more than 8 legs?
   - Yes — it's a centipede
   - No — it's a spider.

23) BB and bb

Revision Summary for B1 Topic 2 (page 28)

16) a) BMI = 58 ÷ (1.5)²
      = 58 ÷ 2.25
      = 25.7777... = 25.8
    b) No, Sophie isn't obese (because her BMI is under 30).

Revision Summary for C1a Topics 1 & 2 (page 49)

21) a) $CaCO_3 + 2HCl \rightarrow CaCl_2 + H_2O + CO_2$
    b) $Ca + 2H_2O \rightarrow Ca(OH)_2 + H_2$

P1a Topic 1 page 72: $v = f \times \lambda = 2375$ m/s

Revision Summary for P1a Topics 1, 2 & 3 (page 88)

4) 20 m

Revision Summary for P1b Topics 4, 5 & 6 (page 104)

11)
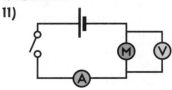
$P = I \times V$

19) a) 2 years
    b) B (payback time is 1.5 years)
    c) $0.1 \times 5 \times 8 = 4p$
25) 70%